The Ultimate Ma.
& Medical Student Šelf-Défense

Human Rights Violations in Medicine

A-to-Z Action Guide

Pamela Wible, M.D.

www.IdealMedicalCare.org

Library of Congress Control Number: 2019906521
ISBN-13: 978-0-9857103-3-0
ISBN-10: 0-9857103-3-0
v1.0 6.19.19

Design & Production: Kassy Daggett, Pamela Wible, M.D.

Editing: Betsy Robinson, Victor Rozek, Sydney Ashland, Jeffery Weisman, J.D., M.D., Ph.D.

Author Photo: GeVe   Illustrations: Vince Palko

Special thanks to all the courageous medical students and physicians
who have allowed me to publish their experiences.

Dedicated to my brothers and sisters in medicine
who have lost their lives in pursuit of healing others.

All book proceeds dedicated to physician suicide prevention.

The Ultimate Manual for Physician
& Medical Student Self-Defense

Human Rights Violations in Medicine

A-to-Z Action Guide

Pamela Wible, M.D.

Pamela Wible, M.D., Publishing
Oregon

Table of Contents

M

N

O

P

Q

R

S

T

U

Introduction

It took her months to speak about him without crying. Her only child hanged himself the morning before his radiology rotation—the specialty he dreamed of pursuing. He had just spent Mother's Day with her the day before. Nobody had any idea.

Cheryl didn't know medical students were at high risk of suicide—until her son Sean was found dead in his apartment. Nobody warned her.

Distraught, she could barely put a sentence together. She couldn't speak on the phone, so she had been emailing me for months. When I finally heard her voice, I was overtaken by anger. I've spoken to hundreds of parents grieving the loss of their children to suicide during medical training. Something about Cheryl grabbed my soul. Her only child. She tried for ten years to get pregnant. Finally, in vitro fertilization was a success. She devoted her life to him. His first words. His first footsteps. Pausing to hold it together, she apologized to me for crying.

Why was she apologizing to me? She deserved an apology. From his school. From my profession. I looked up at my wall—all the photos of medical students and doctors dead by suicide. Now another one. We've known for more than a century that doctors have a high suicide rate. Nothing's been done. I wanted to scream. Yet I held it together for Cheryl.

She told me she'll never have grandchildren. She asked me, "What will I do on Christmas? What about Thanksgiving?"

What could I say?

She felt like her life was over. How could she go on?

She sent me his baby photos. Such a perfect and sweet child raised in a loving family. Sean grew into a responsible, intelligent, compassionate man who wanted to help others—so he decided to pursue medicine.

Parents are swept away with great pride when their child is accepted into medical school. Heroic and noble, their child will save lives. And, they trust their child's life will be safe. Why wouldn't they? Their child will be in the safest place in the world—one of the best academic medical centers, with all the latest technology, surrounded by skilled specialists.

In the year after her son's death, Cheryl and I started a support group for families that lost their children to suicide during medical training. Parents wonder why nobody warned them of the suicide risk. If they had known, maybe they could have saved their child's life. What bothers Cheryl most is that she didn't know.

Cheryl still asks me, "Why don't medical schools warn families?"

Medicine's Hidden Crisis—Suicide

Suicide is an occupational hazard for medical students and physicians.

Walking into medical school is like entering a war zone. A medical student in the Army Reserve told me she was less stressed in Afghanistan during active sniper fire than in medical school! Here's why: She had total trust in her military comrades. She knew if killed by enemy fire, she would be brought home, covered in an American flag, and honored with a proper burial. They had her back. In medical school, she never knew who would stab her in the back.

Students enter medical school with their mental health on par with or better than their peers. So why do so many medical trainees kill themselves before graduation?

I suffered major depression in medical school and almost took my life by suicide as a physician. I thought I was the only one. Then both men I dated in medical school died by suicide—as successful practicing physicians. They left behind wives and young children.

I had to find out why my friends were dying.

In 2012, I began running a suicide helpline for doctors. Since then I've spoken to thousands of suicidal physicians (and families that have lost doctors to suicide). I've now compiled a registry with nearly 1,300 doctor suicides that I've personally investigated.

I know why doctors die by suicide. I know highest-risk specialties. I know what leads doctors and medical students to make the decision to kill themselves during medical training and beyond. Now I feel compelled to share what I've discovered with you.

Suicide censorship perpetuates medical student and doctor suicides. When families don't know the health risks of medical training, they are unable to help their loved ones. Informed consent is required in medicine, yet students and their families don't receive informed consent of the health risks of medical education.

For every medical student and doctor suicide, there are thousands of physicians still suffering the non-fatal wounds of their medical education.

To physician parents like mine—who warn their children not to pursue medicine—these are the wounds you don't want inflicted upon your loved ones. To everyone who doesn't feel quite right after medical training, here are the words that describe your injuries. You've suffered human rights violations. You deserve protection. Here's a guide so you know what to do next.

Step One—Stop Saying "Burnout"

Those who control our language determine our destiny.

For physicians, accurate terminology is paramount when caring for patients. Every word counts. Any language barrier obscures facts and suddenly takes a physician down the wrong diagnostic path. One misinterpreted word could lead to a misdiagnosis. A wrong diagnosis leads to the wrong treatment plan—and our patient may die.

As scientists we must have courage to discern the truth even when it is concealed or opposed. Even if we feel thwarted and misled. Not every patient is a textbook case. The best physicians are detectives—relentless in their quest for the definitive diagnosis and treatment plan. Imagine if smallpox was just called a rash. If we didn't investigate the etiology, we surely wouldn't have eradicated the deadly disease.

Truth ultimately prevails. Our task is to discover the truth before patients die. In medicine, there's no time for guessing. No time for confusion. When urgent action is required, even hesitation may be deadly. In an epidemic, a misdiagnosis may lead to the loss of hundreds of thousands of lives.

The latest epidemic in health care is called physician "burnout." That's what we're told. Yet physician "burnout" is a misnomer—a victim-blaming term that obscures the truth and distracts us from the real epidemic—physician suicide—fueled by human rights violations in medicine.

Human rights abuse conjures up images of genocide, torture, and war. So some physicians prefer to replace "burnout" with "moral injury"—a less inflammatory combination of words than human rights violations. Moral injury is damage to one's conscience when perpetuating, witnessing, or failing to prevent acts that violate a person's values. Unlike human rights violations, moral injury is subjective and has no medical or legal solution.

Words like "burnout" and "moral injury" distract and confuse victims. One or two well-placed words can cover up what we're not supposed to see.

Each year more than one million Americans lose their doctors to suicide in a public health crisis hidden from us all. A public health crisis requires precise language, daily body counts, clear communication, and a serious action plan with breaking news updates on all major networks.

Another doctor dies by suicide and—nothing.

It takes courage to ask why so many doctors are dying. Why doctors kill themselves at three times the rate of the general public.

Despite all the physician "burnout" workshops, books, and experts, the number of doctors suffering from cynicism, exhaustion, despair, and injured morals is mounting. Lavender spritzes, deep breathing exercises, and resilience modules haven't worked. Why?

We've been misled. We're on the wrong treatment plan.

Physician "burnout" conveniently deflects attention from widespread abuse perpetrated by the medical system while labeling physician victims as defective. A clever strategy by those who prefer to avoid accountability for inhumane working conditions while appointing chief wellness officers to enforce wellness on the abused.

Since 2015, I've been debunking "burnout," yet victims can't seem to give it up. Doctors keep asking, "What word can we use to replace physician 'burnout?'"

Try three: human rights violations.

Human Rights Violations in Medicine

Human rights are universal moral principles that apply to the treatment of all human beings no matter sex, ethnicity, religion, culture, *or profession*. These basic freedoms are standards of human behavior protected by law from birth until death.

In 1948 the Universal Declaration of Human Rights set the international standards for human rights so we might have freedom, justice, and peace in our world. Individual nations have also drafted documents to safeguard the rights of their citizens. Since I am a practicing physician in the United States, I reference not only the Universal Declaration of Human Rights, but also the United States Constitution, the United States Civil Rights Act, and the Americans with Disabilities Act as guidelines for human behavior.

As physicians, our professional code of conduct further dictates that we uphold the rights of the most vulnerable. Despite being held to the highest standards of behavior when safeguarding the rights of patients, physicians and medical students experience human rights violations endangering their own lives.

I've been reporting on human rights violations in medicine since 2014. Now I've compiled five years of my research into one handy self-defense manual for you. So what are the major human rights violations in medicine?

Physicians-in-training are now legally forced to work 28-hour shifts and 80-hour work weeks. They suffer extreme sleep deprivation at levels incompatible with human life leading to hallucinations, psychosis, seizures—and death. During these inhumane shifts, doctors experience food and water deprivation. Hypoglycemia and dehydration lead to fatigue, confusion, dizziness, and fainting. Physicians are not immune to the basic laws of human physiology.

Bullying and hazing persist in medical education despite being outlawed from elementary schools through universities. I receive ongoing reports of racial and sexual harassment inside our most prestigious teaching hospitals. Most shocking, our nation's hospitals and medical schools continue to discriminate against physicians and medical students with mental illness and physical disabilities—contrary to their stated mission to provide compassionate care for all.

Medical students and physicians develop high rates of occupationally induced anxiety, depression, PTSD, and suicidal ideation. Yet we're offered no debriefing or on-the-job support after witnessing trauma and death. Instead we risk interrogation and punishment by medical boards, hospitals, and insurance companies when seeking mental health care. As physicians, we comply with laws protecting our patients' medical information; however, our confidentiality is often breached by hospitals and medical boards when we receive care. As a result, doctors either don't receive needed care or drive hundreds of miles out of town, use fake names, and pay cash for psychiatric treatment.

Censorship—loss of freedom of speech—is common during medical training and practice. Physicians and medical students are scrutinized on personal social media accounts and often fear sharing divergent views due to retaliation from superiors.

In the aftermath of medical student and physician suicides, surviving colleagues have been threatened with termination, intimidated to keep quiet, and obstructed from peaceably assembling to grieve the loss of their own friends. Doctors and medical students have also been prohibited from attending funerals for their immediate family members.

Trainees have no time to build healthy relationships, date, and procreate during their fertile years when they are overworked by the equivalent of two to three full-time jobs. If they do conceive, they may suffer harassment while pregnant, breastfeeding, or requiring time to care for their kids. Medical training places severe physiologic stress on the mother, leading to life-threatening complications of pregnancy and fetal death.

Doctors are routinely exposed to unethical and criminal behavior in clinics and hospitals, including insurance fraud. Some are forced to do procedures without proper supervision or patient consent. Resident physicians are coerced to lie on their time logs if they work more than 80 hours weekly, or be punished for duty-hour violations and labeled as "inefficient," then forced to see psychiatrists where they are diagnosed with ADD and prescribed stimulants to pick up their pace.

United States hospitals and clinics routinely violate the human rights of medical students and physicians, endangering their lives—and the lives of their patients. Physician-induced medical mistakes are the third leading cause of death in the United States. Physicians who attempt to protect their patients by complaining about human rights violations risk retaliation and destruction of their careers.

So why am I writing a book on human rights violations in medical training? Not to bash my profession. I'm writing this action guide to empower my brothers and sisters in medicine, to save the lives of future generations of physicians—and to salvage my beloved profession.

Please join me in speaking up against abuse.

"Truth is belligerent in the face of injustice."

~ Pamela Wible, M.D.

A-to-Z Action Guide Instructions

Here's the ultimate manual for physician and medical student self-defense—a pocket-guide for surviving medical training and practice without dying by suicide so you can love your life as a physician. For ease of reference, human rights violations are arranged alphabetically by chapter, each with specific action steps. These are the top 40 chapters on human rights abuse in medicine I've compiled from thousands of hours of phone calls with struggling medical students and physicians over the last seven years while operating a free suicide helpline. Please note that this is not a comprehensive list. If you encounter violations that are not yet covered in this book, please submit them confidentially to IdealMedicalCare.org.

Begin by reviewing <u>Human Rights Violations Definitions</u> and <u>Documentation Guidelines</u> to ensure that you are prepared to document violations for optimal legal protection. Many medical students and physicians experience more than one type of human rights violation. If you are uncomfortable, yet unsure whether you are experiencing a violation of your rights, please track those events in <u>Uncomfortable Situations</u> on page 184, then match them with the appropriate chapter later. Be alert to subtle abuse that can escalate over time.

Keep this action guide in your white-coat pocket or on your nightstand so you can track your experiences daily during medical training and practice. Identify violations that you experience each day and then follow specific action steps to resolve the abuse—for yourself and for future generations of physicians at your institution. If you are a practicing physician, review chapters to identify violations you have endured in the past. Document your memories. You may be surprised to discover that you are currently suffering long-term effects from human rights violations you sustained years ago. Your newfound insight and understanding will allow you to heal so you can recover your passion for medicine and enjoy your life.

Medical school was traumatic for me, though I loved my residency. During my training and career I have experienced 20 of these human rights violations. I've spent more on therapy to heal from my training than I spent on medical school tuition.

At the end of the book (page 214) you'll have an opportunity to identify the number of human rights violations you have sustained, and calculate your Wible Human Rights Violations Inventory Number (WHR-VIN). Then you can take action by completing an <u>Addendum to My Hippocratic Oath</u>. Now is your time to heal. May this book be your guide.

For medical professionals in other countries who may experience even more extreme human rights violations than American medical students and physicians, do not despair. Please know the basic formula is the same, though your action steps in each chapter may vary depending on the laws of your country.

My hope is that all medical students and physicians across the globe utilize this action guide to finally eradicate human rights violations in medicine. Please share with medical professionals and their families. Bulk shipments are available for residency programs, medical schools, and hospitals. May we all join together and heal our profession. Thank you for caring.

Human Rights Violations
Definitions

From sex trafficking to censorship, the range of human rights violations is immense, some more heinous than others. Abuse may be perpetrated by dictators in war-torn countries and administrators in first-world hospitals. Here's a partial list of violations present in our most prestigious medical institutions. In isolation, many seem minor. In totality, these violations lead to thousands of American medical student, physician, and patient deaths— each year.

Anti-Assembly ~ *Prohibiting medical students and physicians from gathering peacefully for a common purpose.*

Bullying ~ *Repeated and intentional abuse of power to control vulnerable medical students and/or physicians.*

Censorship ~ *Prohibiting free speech of medical students or physicians, including obstruction of communication via social media, films, or books considered threatening to medical hierarchy.*

Confidentiality Breach ~ *When a medical student's or physician's sensitive and private information is intentionally disclosed or acquired by a third party such as an employer or medical institution that has power over the victim's medical career.*

Corruption ~ *Misuse of power for personal profit from fraudulent business practices that violate the rights of medical professionals and/or their patients.*

Discrimination, Mental Health Disability ~ *Mistreatment by a medical institution/employer of a medical professional with a mental health disability protected by anti-discrimination law.*

Discrimination, Physical Disability ~ *Mistreatment by a medical institution/employer of a medical professional with a physical disability protected by anti-discrimination law.*

Discrimination, Racial ~ *Mistreatment by a medical institution/employer of a medical professional based upon race protected by anti-discrimination law.*

Discrimination, Sexual ~ *Mistreatment by a medical institution/employer of a medical professional based upon gender protected by anti-discrimination law.*

Exploitation ~ *Profiteering or benefiting from the mistreatment or abuse of a medical student or physician.*

Food Deprivation ~ *Lack of access to food essential for normal function of the human body of a medical professional.*

Forced Drugging ~ *Medication (usually psychotropics) forced upon a physician or medical student under duress as a requirement of employment or education.*

Gaslighting ~ *Psychological manipulation of a medical student or physician leading the victim to question their own sanity.*

Harassment, Disability ~ *Unwelcome or offensive conduct based upon a disability that creates a hostile work environment for a medical professional.*

Harassment, Racial ~ *Unwelcome or offensive conduct based upon race that creates a hostile work environment for a medical professional.*

Harassment, Sexual ~ *Unwelcome or offensive sexual conduct that creates a hostile work environment for a medical professional.*

Hazing ~ *Humiliating and dangerous rituals imposed upon medical students and physician trainees as part of their medical education.*

Illegal Activity ~ *Unlawful acts required of medical professionals to maintain employment or educational trajectory.*

Intimidation ~ *Terrorizing medical trainees in the guise of medical education to maintain power and control over students and physicians-in-training.*

J-1 Visa Abuse ~ *Human rights violations against foreign medical trainees or physicians who risk deportation when they don't submit to mistreatment.*

Joking ~ *Humor that violates the humanity of patients, medical students, or physicians.*

Karōshi ~ *Physician death by overwork.*

Karojishi ~ *Physician suicide by overwork.*

Lying ~ *Perpetuating false statements that may endanger medical professionals and their patients.*

Maternal Deprivation ~ *Lack of access to a mother in medical training, leading to adverse health sequelae in mother, child, or fetal death.*

No Mental Health Care ~ *Absence of psychological support for medical professionals with occupationally induced emotional distress who are penalized with loss or restriction of career for seeking help.*

Overwork ~ *Complete mental and/or physical exhaustion in medical professionals from too much work.*

Pimping ~ *A traditional teaching technique in which a medical trainee is publicly interrogated on medical minutiae until they cry in front of peers, staff, and patients.*

Punishment when Sick ~ *Penalizing a medical student or physician for developing a medical illness.*

Question Quashing ~ *Mistreating medical students or physicians for asking questions resulting in question phobia among victims and witnesses.*

Retaliation ~ *An adverse action taken against a medical student or physician who exercises a protected legal right.*

Sleep Deprivation ~ *Extreme lack of sleep that may lead to the injury or death of medical professionals and their patients.*

Suicide ~ *Wrongful death of a medical trainee or physician subjected to human rights violations in medicine.*

Termination, Wrongful ~ *Illegal termination (or dismissal from medical school) in violation of a medical student's or physician's rights or contract.*

Threat ~ *A declaration of intent to inflict punishment upon a medical student or physician in retribution for an (in)action.*

Unethical Activity ~ *Immoral, dishonest, or deceitful activities forced upon a medical student or physician as part of their education or employment.*

Violence ~ *The intentional use of physical force to injure a medical student or physician.*

Water Deprivation ~ *Lack of access to hydration essential for normal function of the human body of a medical professional.*

Xenophobia ~ *Prejudice against medical students or physicians from other cultures.*

Yelling ~ *Shouting at a medical student or doctor.*

Zombification ~ *The process of dehumanizing a medical trainee to produce a compliant robotic doctor.*

Human Rights Violations Documentation Guidelines

Medical liability cases are won or lost on documentation. Without a comprehensive medical record, you can't defend yourself. To protect yourself as a medical professional, you must also document violations of your human rights by any medical institution or individual. Incidents that escalate over several years are challenging to prove without documentation. Many protections of your rights will be lost if you fail to act within the statute of limitations. Do not delay in your documentation and action. Do not naively assume things will get better. By waiting, you increase your chance of further abuse and risk perpetuating a culture that continues victimizing others at your institution. Your career and future are on the line. Do not wait until you are mistreated to the point of being forced out of your hospital or training program. Protect your career and take action early!

TAKE ACTION NOW

1. Document everything. Write a memo to yourself describing any interaction that makes you feel uncomfortable. Note the date and time and everyone present. Email it to yourself using a personal email address.

2. Record everything. Use your cell phone to audio record the abuser (remember many cell phone apps will turn off if you receive a phone call so

use airplane mode). Alternatively, order a cheap key chain USB recording device to capture all interactions so you have detailed documentation of the encounter. **Note: In the United States crimes are legal to record. Crimes evolve over time. When in doubt, press record.**

3. Forward all work emails to a personal HIPAA-compliant account. Medical professionals who receive harassing work emails or text messages may have their work accounts deactivated by their employer in an attempt to destroy incriminating evidence to protect an abuser. Always protect confidential patient information and do not violate HIPAA.

4. Make at least two additional copies of all documentation. In addition to your personal computer, consider an online cloud storage option and send a USB drive to a trusted friend or family member to keep for you. Store one in a safe deposit box for added security.

5. Ask other residents or hospital employees if they are experiencing the same types of mistreatment and document their personal contact information in case other victims leave your medical institution and you need to reach them.

6. Many medical professionals don't realize that the objective of Human Resources is to protect the company or hospital. They may pressure a victim to inappropriately confront a perpetrator or sign documents that could hurt their legal case. Keep copies of any paperwork presented to you. **Never sign any documents under duress without the advice of your own attorney.**

7. Document all internal efforts to report and resolve human rights violations at your medical institution. Include dates and times of your meetings with Human Resources or your ombudsman. Many academic medical centers have an ombudsman that acts as a confidential advocate. Most take their job seriously and may help you identify an attorney. Some break confidentiality.

8. Document meetings with potential attorneys and their advice. Hire an attorney with experience defending medical students, residents, and physicians, as law pertaining to each of these groups can be complex. Consider hiring a JD/MD (or DO) who understands personally the abuses of medical training. Many attorneys will work on contingency and only take a percentage of fees from a successful lawsuit.

9. Each time you are evaluated or hospitalized, immediately request a copy of your medical records. If you are obstructed in any way from receiving medical records within 30 days of your request, seek legal counsel. Medical institutions have been guilty of withholding and altering evidence.

10. Download copies of medical institution handbooks, employee contracts, and other documents related to your employment or education.

11. You have the right to a safe workplace. If your workplace is unsafe, unhealthful, or hazardous, file a confidential OSHA (Occupational Safety and Health Administration) complaint to trigger an on-site inspection by a compliance officer trained to protect workers and their rights. Then request a health hazard evaluation through NIOSH (National Institute for Occupational Safety and Health). They will perform an assessment on physician work conditions and file a report with recommendations. Three employees are required to request a NIOSH evaluation. **Your identity will remain confidential.**

After Consulting with Your Attorney

1. Schedule a meeting with your department chief, program director, or Human Resources if you have not already done so. Documenting these interactions in detail will place you under protected activity from retaliation.

2. File a formal complaint with EEOC (Equal Employment Opportunity Commission) if you have experienced discrimination, harassment, or retaliation against a protected group (reference relevant chapters on

each). If you plan to sue under title VII of the Civil Rights Act, you must file a formal EEOC complaint first. Many people misunderstand the website and file a preliminary charge rather than a formal complaint. Deadlines are 180 to 300 days from date of incident and vary by state.

3. You may also contact other federal agencies that will investigate your complaint. These agencies may include the Department of Education and/or Health and Human Services Office of Civil Rights. Please note the Department of Education might only investigate incidents going back 180 days but you have longer to file a lawsuit.

4. Document a report to the ACGME (Accreditation Council of Graduate Medical Education) if you are in residency training. Have your attorney submit an official complaint letter to force the ACGME to be on notice. Please do not expect the ACGME to take action to protect you. Giving an informal warning to a program or even placing them on "ACGME probation" does little to help a resident.

5. If you are a medical student, file a complaint with the LCME (Liaison Committee of Medical Education), the accrediting agency for medical schools in the United States and Canada.

6. Have your attorney draft a demand letter; it places your program on notice of legal violations and indicates you are serious and will defend yourself.

7. File a lawsuit to leave a paper trail that is indisputable. Retaliation will be very clear when you have an active legal case against the hospital or medical institution.

Document Your Actions

_____

_____

_____

_____

_____

_____

_____

_____

_____

_____

_____

_____

_____

_____

_____

_____

_____

_____

_____

_____

_____

_____

_____

_____

_____

_____

_____

_____

_____

_____

_____

_____

_____

_____

_____

_____

A-to-Z Action Guide

- FOOD & WATER DEPRIVATION
- PUNISHMENT WHEN SICK
- SLEEP DEPRIVATION
- BULLYING
- HARASSMENT
- VIOLENCE
- PIMPING
- RACISM
- SEXISM

Anti-Assembly

Prohibiting medical students and physicians from gathering peacefully for a common purpose.

After the 2016 suicide of a second-year female anesthesiology resident at Duke, several faculty complained about their department's widespread discrimination against female anesthesiologists and their refusal to support staff mental health, according to a federal lawsuit. While the department chair maintained they held no liability in the resident's suicide, many faculty, visibly upset, felt the focus should have been to help grieving staff heal from the tragedy. Faculty member, Dr. Cheryl Jones, met with surviving residents to offer her support—at which point the chair warned faculty they were prohibited from gathering with residents without approval from the program director. Dr. Jones was also prohibited from organizing a candlelight vigil to mourn the resident who had died, and subsequently she was forced out of the department.

Prestigious medical institutions throughout the United States have similarly prohibited the peaceful public gathering of students and physicians to mourn a colleague's suicide—even actively preventing them from attending funerals.

"A third-year psychiatry resident from our children's hospital killed himself by overdose," shares one physician. "We were all forbidden from attending his funeral because our pediatric chief told us, 'Suicide is an occupational hazard of this job. You need to come to work and do your job.'"

Amid tragedy, Americans assemble publicly to grieve. After school shootings, we bring balloons and teddy bears. We wave flags to honor our fallen police and firefighters. Even drunk drivers get roadside crosses. In a world full of public memorials, where are the vigils and flowers for our fallen physicians?

I've spent seven years investigating nearly 1,300 doctor suicides. Most are buried in secrecy and shame by our own medical institutions. No vigils. No flowers. No public memorials.

In 2018, Dr. Deelshad Joomun stepped off the rooftop of a Mount Sinai Health System building that houses hundreds of resident physicians. Within one hour of her suicide, I received three emails. (Google "Suicided doctor: covered up with a tarp—and silence" to read emails.) The authors were distraught about yet another doctor dead on the sidewalk in front of their building. Upset about the silence, secrecy, and lack of support for surviving colleagues—*they begged me for help*—to investigate the deplorable working conditions in Manhattan hospitals and to lead a memorial for the deceased doctor.

I flew to New York City to lead her candlelight vigil and ten-hour memorial (to give residents ample time to participate). Several residents confided they were afraid to attend due to threatening emails suggesting termination of their contracts.

As we assembled at the site of Dr. Joomun's suicide, I was informed by staff in the building that any media at the memorial would be arrested. Yet our freedom as Americans to gather peacefully is protected by the First Amendment of the United States Constitution, as is freedom of the press. Both are essential to a democracy. Arresting the press would guarantee more media coverage of a hospital's attempt to censor a suicide memorial. Footage from her memorial is now part of a documentary that honors the lives of nearly 100 doctors who have died by suicide. Thankfully, the videographer wasn't arrested. (Visit DoNoHarmFilm.com to view film trailer.)

As United States citizens, we have an inalienable birthright to peacefully gather in public forums to express ourselves for any purpose without obstruction. In 1948, Article 20 of the Universal Declaration of Human Rights made this freedom a global right for all people. Freedom of peaceful assembly is not only a human right, it's a political right, a civil liberty—and in the aftermath of a suicide, a medical necessity. An organized postvention response involving a public vigil and memorial facilitates individual and community healing from grief and decreases the risk of suicide among survivors (including bystanders who witness suicides). Suicide is a well-known occupational hazard for physicians, yet most medical institutions still lack any organized suicide prevention and postvention programs.

In obstetrics when an otherwise healthy mom died unexpectedly, one hospital brought in grief counselors for an all-day event. But why no support after a doctor's sudden death? To provide no postvention for colleagues and to actively prohibit a memorial service is abhorrent and contradicts the healing mission of our health care facilities.

Like all survivors of tragedy, medical students and doctors must unite as a community to express themselves—particularly after the loss of a peer. As Americans, medical professionals have the right to hold public meetings and to form associations with whomever they want without interference from medical institutions, employers, or the government. We also have the right to publicly protest—a privilege physicians underutilize to our detriment.

TAKE ACTION NOW

1. Utilize your right to freely assemble by participating in public meetings, boycotts, and rallies.

2. Unite. Supporting one another by assembling protects individuals from being targeted for their convictions.

3. Unionize. All physician employees have the right to unionize.

4. Join with colleagues to host a candlelight vigil and memorial for medical students and physicians who have died by suicide. Organize an ongoing postvention support group for survivors grieving a colleague's suicide.

5. If your right to public assembly has been violated, gather evidence and document the violation. Reference <u>Human Rights Violations Documentation Guidelines</u>.

Document Anti-Assembly Actions

Bullying

Repeated and intentional abuse of power to control vulnerable medical students and/or physicians.

Bright-eyed students begin medical training with passion and exuberance for learning. Soon that excitement may dissipate into fear. Article 26 of the Universal Declaration of Human Rights proclaims: "Education shall be directed to the full development of the human personality and to the strengthening of respect for human rights and fundamental freedoms." Yet Western medical education often greets learners with rigid hierarchy and antiquated fear-driven teaching methods in an atmosphere of ruthless competition that pits students against one another for professional survival.

Bullying often begins in lecture halls, during hospital rounds, and in operating rooms with groups of bystanders who witness the event. Large groups allow the bully to create an illusion of mass support and make it less likely for any one person to protest the mistreatment. Most witnesses cower on the sidelines hoping to avoid being the next victim.

A surgery resident shares her long-term mental health sequelae of bullying: "Sometimes I can still hear those attendings in my head saying things like, 'Watching you operate is like watching a retarded monkey' or 'Do they even teach anatomy at your medical school? Our students know more than you!' It's paralyzing. I am reaching out to you for two reasons: I'm interested in eradicating the abuse in medical education. I'd like to have a career in academics and to influence policy regarding the treatment of trainees. More importantly, can you help me make the flashbacks stop?"

"I had emotional whiplash in residency," reports a solo family physician, "Attendings would gang up on one resident and say, 'You're destined to fail. You're lazy.' I received scathing reviews about 'attitude' and 'difficulty with authority.' I remember standing in my bedroom having these crazy panic attacks and thinking I could not go on. They stopped picking on me after a few months and picked on someone else, but I'd see it and it would make me sick. I personally know of one resident in every class who became suicidal while I was there. One had a car 'accident' and died going off a cliff but we all wondered if that was actually an accident."

Bully professors remain in power positions and continue to torment surviving students—even in the aftermath of losing their friends to suicide. One female physician reports, "After one of our residents killed himself, two of my professors sought me out to gloat that their abuse had resulted in his death. They were proud of it."

An old-school pediatrician reveals a creative solution. "We had a professor who would bully us during his lectures. He'd point to somebody in the back of the room and tell them to stop doing what they were doing and pay attention or else! Our class knew there was nobody in the back making noise. Nobody was discourteous. We checked with the upperclassmen and discovered this had been his routine all along—bullying the class into submission. We decided that we would not put up with this. The next time, we called him on it. The president of our class stood up and told him, 'We know what you are doing. There is nobody in the back making noise. We are not staying in your lecture. We are leaving.' And we got up en masse—*all 160 students*—and we walked to the dean's office and reported this. We never saw the professor again."

I asked, "What would you recommend today for medical students who experience bullying?"

His advice: "Call them on it. The only way to combat bullying is to call it out publicly so everybody recognizes it. Do not let anyone intimidate you—ever."

By not challenging the bully culture, we medical professionals accept and support the behavior as the norm passed down to the next generation of trainees. We allow the abuse cycle to persist—even beyond formal medical training. Physicians are groomed as medical students to comply with a lifetime of bullying from insurance companies, employers, and third parties that profit from our disempowerment.

TAKE ACTION NOW

1. Unite with students and physicians to boycott bully professors, attendings, and medical institutions that abuse their staff.

2. Implement a zero-tolerance bullying initiative. Immediately report all bullying so future students are never injured during their education.

3. Always speak up for bully victims. They are at higher risk of suicide.

4. Be the change in your school, clinic, or hospital. Cultures and systems will change when people inside those systems change.

5. Document every instance of bullying at your medical institution with date, time, circumstances, witnesses, and outcome.

Document Bullying

_____

_____

_____

_____

_____

_____

_____

_____

_____

Censorship

Prohibiting free speech of medical students or physicians, including obstruction of communication via social media, films, or books considered threatening to medical hierarchy.

The First Amendment of the United States Constitution guarantees freedom of speech for all citizens as does Article 19 of the Universal Declaration of Human Rights which confirms that "everyone has the right to freedom of opinion and expression; this right includes freedom to hold opinions without interference and to seek, receive and impart information and ideas through any media and regardless of frontiers."

No employer or medical institution has the right to restrict freedom of thought or expression by medical students and physicians. We have the right to freely make up our own minds, to think what we like, to say what we think, and to share ideas with each other and our patients.

High doctor suicide rates were first reported in 1858. Yet root causes remain unaddressed—largely due to censorship by medical institutions. Suicides are hidden with a range of euphemisms that may blame or defame victims. Surviving colleagues have been threatened with termination, sabotaged letters of reference, false unprofessionalism claims—even bullied with forced psychiatric evaluations if they question the cause of their colleague's suicide.

After the suicides of a former internal medicine doctor who had just started his fellowship, and a current anesthesiology resident (in which no grief counseling was offered), Duke faculty member, Dr. Cheryl Jones, was blocked from organizing a vigil. She then attempted to distribute six copies of my book *Physician Suicide Letters—Answered* to help her grieving residents when she was physically obstructed by her superiors. The books were stolen from the hospital workroom where she placed them and banned from the department. Dr. Jones was then summoned to the office of the division chief (who stole the books) and was told not to distribute them to the residents. Mishandling of suicides at Duke (and my banned book) are now part of a federal lawsuit.

In 2015, after the AMA invited me to deliver my TEDMED talk, I was disinvited shortly before the event because they were "uncomfortable" with the topic of physician suicide.

At a prestigious United States teaching hospital, the head of psychiatry declined to show a documentary on doctor suicide prevention at her hospital because she feared an uprising among residents. A physician friend was fired from her psychiatry residency for hosting a doctor suicide awareness day. Medical trainees have been told to remove articles about doctor suicide from their personal social media accounts by superiors who are breaching the constitutional rights of their employees.

Residents and medical students who have suffered from bullying and disability discrimination at their medical institutions have been forced to sign nondisclosure agreements to permanently obstruct their rights to share how terribly they were mistreated. One mother accepted an honorary diploma after her son's suicide in return for a signed nondisclosure agreement with the medical school that now prevents her from speaking about her own child's suicide.

TAKE ACTION NOW

1. Never sign a nondisclosure agreement censoring your right to speak the truth of your experiences.

2. Report organizations that breach your constitutional right to an attorney who will stop the censorship at your institution to protect you and future generations of medical professionals.

3. Document (with audio, print, screenshots, photographs) any effort on the part of an employer, hospital, or medical school to limit your freedom of speech. Reference Human Rights Violations Documentation Guidelines.

Document Censorship

_____

_____

_____

_____

_____

_____

_____

_____

_____

_____

_____

_____

_____

_____

_____

_____

_____

_____

_____

_____

_____

_____

_____

_____

_____

_____

Confidentiality Breach

When a medical student's or physician's sensitive and private information is intentionally disclosed or acquired by a third party such as an employer or medical institution that has power over the victim's medical career.

HIPAA (Health Insurance Portability and Accountability Act) is United States legislation that provides data privacy and security provisions to safeguard medical information for all American citizens.

Information about health status, provision of health care, or payment for health care that is collected by a covered entity (such as a doctor or health center) and can be linked to a specific individual is considered PHI (Protected Health Information) under United States law. Medical professionals go to great lengths to safeguard PHI of patients or face harsh penalties. However, medical students and physicians don't seem to enjoy the same protections.

Confidentiality breaches of medical students' and physicians' protected health information is common during medical training and beyond. Most obvious are the invasive mental health questions on applications for state medical licensing, hospital privileges, and insurance contracting. Doctors may be required to turn over their "confidential" medical records to non-physicians who may control their careers. State medical boards demand to read doctors' mental health records and may exclude physicians from practicing medicine in a particular state. Hospitals demand to read doctors' mental health records and may exclude physicians from hospital staff privileges. Insurance plans demand to read doctors' mental health records and may exclude physicians from insurance contracts.

"The insurance credentialing staff are the worst!" shares one psychiatrist. "They have sent unencrypted emails with my social security number, driver's license, and health history to the wrong email addresses. Then they blame me for misspelling my name in the email (even though it is on every page of their credentialing document)."

Insurance credentialing applications protect insurance companies. Employment applications protect employers. Hospital privilege applications protect hospitals. Medical boards exist to protect the public. HIPAA protects patients. So who protects physicians and medical students from breaches of confidentiality?

Hospitalized physicians often experience HIPAA violations in which their colleagues and employers suddenly have access to their personal health information. Program directors show up in their hospital rooms to discuss everything from their cesarean-section to their suicide attempt and, of course, speed up their discharge to get them back on the call schedule.

An intern was hospitalized for diverticulitis while on duty and later was presented on rounds to the other residents, interns, and medical students.

"I had my cancer surgery in the hospital where I worked. My superior told my coworkers I lied about having cancer. People looked up my records to 'see how sick I really was.' I had the IT department put an extra layer of security on my records but even after that people managed to get into them," explains a physician friend who was ultimately fired from her psychiatry residency in retaliation for getting cancer. Reference <u>Discrimination, Physical Health Disability</u> for details.

A new physician mom reports, "A male colleague said, 'Wow, sounds like you had a horrible delivery. How can you even walk properly after that?' I was speechless. Part of me is still tempted to sue for HIPAA violation."

In China, physicians have mandatory yearly physicals in their own hospitals (including IUD checks during the one-child limit era). Colleagues perform their breast and pelvic exams with zero privacy of health records.

After an American medical student's suicide attempt, the dean showed up in the student's hospital room to discuss his upcoming graduation (which he failed to attend after he completed his suicide on discharge). Imagine a real estate agent having her boss show up in her hospital room after a suicide attempt to discuss an open house, or a truck driver post-prostate surgery having his employer appear in the recovery room to get him back on the highway. Only medical professionals face this level of personal life invasion.

"During medical school they used my real psychiatric medical record as a 'sample patient' during EMR training because the trainer thought my last name was funny," shares a physician friend who reveals, "I don't know how many other groups he trained with my psych records."

If doctors develop mental health issues that lead to license restrictions, their PHI may be placed on their public record in an online database accessible through their medical board. In many states a print version lands in all doctors' mailboxes quarterly—a public shaming document disclosing all sorts of sensitive and personal things about their peers that is quite frankly nobody's business. Yet doctors read these reports like tabloid news in fear they could be next.

"The Medical Board of California has publicized my diagnosis of PTSD on their website," explains one female physician. "Not only did they publicize it but they distorted the background and used it to claim that I had a long history of mental health issues that led to my failure in residency. I didn't fail. I was kicked out of the program for giving a presentation on workplace bullying and gender inequality."

"I got in trouble for a boundary violation in residency," shares a male physician, "and the medical board included my protected health information on my public citation, now available on the World Wide Web for people to download."

Psychiatric evaluations may be forced on residents who are labeled as "inefficient" or "unprofessional." Placed on psychiatric medication under duress, trainees are suddenly "diagnosed" with psychiatric illnesses that may land on their official records to censor them in retaliation for asking questions that their program directors don't want them to ask. Reference Forced Drugging for details.

TAKE ACTION NOW

1. Be wary when forced to see a "preferred" psychiatrist by your employer or program director. Your confidential and protected health information may be breached.

2. Ask the medical professional attending to your care if indeed your records will be maintained in confidence.

3. Elect to receive mental health care from your own psychiatrist who you choose outside of your medical institution (not one mandated by a third party).

4. Never sign a contract that forces you to receive care under any program that breaches your confidentiality or mandates that you waive your HIPAA rights.

5. Avoid receiving medical care in the hospital where you work—or you may be presented on grand rounds!

6. File a formal HIPAA violation complaint with the Office for Civil Rights within 180 days of any confidentiality breach.

7. Document all breaches of confidentiality. Reference <u>Human Rights Violations Documentation Guidelines</u>.

Document Confidentiality Breaches

_____

_____

_____

_____

_____

_____

Corruption

Misuse of power for personal profit from fraudulent business practices that violate the rights of medical professionals and/or their patients.

Physicians often pursue medicine as idealistic humanitarians motivated by a deep spiritual calling to help and heal others. Doctors want to follow the rules and do the right thing for patients. After completing their lengthy medical training and amassing hundreds of thousands of dollars in educational debt, physicians too often find themselves as unsuspecting accomplices in criminal rings that financially exploit the most vulnerable patients.

Dr. Steven Ortiz, a beloved spine surgeon, couldn't play the game of corruption—harming patients for profit. In 2017, he was found dead at his hospital of a self-inflicted gunshot wound to the heart. He died by suicide as a whistleblower to draw attention to fraudulent practices that were injuring the lives of patients.

In his goodbye email, he thanked the nursing staff for taking excellent care of his patients and he explains, "I left my past practice because the surgeons were doing unnecessary surgery, and now I have landed in a place where I am coerced to withhold care from patients. Just can't win. So, after all that, I've decided to check out."

Dr. Ortiz asked other physicians for help—even met with the hospital board of directors—and he was told to just "go with the flow." He sought out government officials and the FBI. He never heard back from them. He explored (and documented) all his options. Exhausted, he saw no solution. He was not depressed. He was frustrated, pissed, and stuck. He truly felt that his suicide was the only way to draw attention to—and end—the corruption.

In the aftermath of his suicide, flyers were taped on hospital walls naming the doctors responsible for his death and demanding justice, yet Dr. Ortiz is just one of tens of thousands of doctors trapped in corrupt health systems, caught between for-profit insurers, unethical administrators, and shareholders demanding maximum profit extraction from the sick. Physicians are the extraction device. Without a proper investigation of the corruption leading to this surgeon's suicide, it's impossible to protect patients or prevent the next doctor suicide.

Our medical system profits off physician labor and compliance with corruption. Trainees are taught to misuse power for profit by fraudulently increasing documentation to upcode for inflated billing and then downcode their work hour logs to comply with 80-hour work weeks. Hospitals bankroll off unsupervised residents billing at top codes per patient while exploiting physicians-in-training as cheap labor, earning less than minimum wage when accounting for their actual 100-plus hour work weeks.

Doctors are constantly asked to do things they find unethical: "I was asked to lie on autopsy reports to protect surgeons from malpractice lawsuits (which I didn't)," shares one physician. "And all of that caused me to fall into major depression."

TAKE ACTION NOW

1. Never participate in altering medical records or insurance fraud—a crime with severe penalties that has led to physician suicides. When refusing to participate, document the situation as it is more challenging to dispute your evidence when documented.

2. Unite with and help other medical professionals who have been victims of criminal health systems.

3. Contact an attorney skilled in medical fraud and corruption.

4. Notify insurance companies, including Medicare, of fraudulent claims and they will perform an audit at your medical institution. Reference <u>Retaliation</u> for protection.

5. Document all corruption, and coercion to participate in corruption. Reference <u>Human Rights Violations Documentation Guidelines</u>.

Document Corruption

_____

_____

_____

_____

_____

_____

_____

_____

_____

_____

_____

_____

_____

_____

_____

_____

_____

_____

_____

_____

_____

_____

Discrimination, Mental Health Disability

Mistreatment by a medical institution/employer of a medical professional with a mental health disability protected by anti-discrimination law.

The Universal Declaration of Human Rights, Article 2, proclaims: "Everyone is entitled to all the rights and freedoms set forth in this Declaration, without distinction of any kind, such as race, color, sex, language, religion, political or other opinion, national or social origin, property, birth or other status."

Our United States Civil Rights Act of 1964, Title VII, also declares: "It shall be an unlawful employment practice for an employer to fail or refuse to hire or to discharge any individual, or otherwise to discriminate against any individual with respect to compensation, terms, conditions, or privileges of employment, because of such individual's race, color, religion, sex, or national origin."

Expanding upon the Civil Rights Act is the Americans with Disabilities Act of 1990 that states: "No covered entity shall discriminate against a qualified individual on the basis of disability in regard to job application procedures, the hiring, advancement, or discharge of employees, employee compensation, job training, and other terms, conditions, and privileges of employment." Despite these protections, physicians are subjected to a continual onslaught of invasive mental health questions throughout their careers.

A physician friend experienced a six-month delay in obtaining her state license when she disclosed that she sought counseling during a divorce. The board mandated that she provide her counseling records. Since her divorce was decades ago (and her counselor had retired) they forced her to undergo a psychiatric evaluation before declaring her safe to practice in the state.

"After passing my board of medicine exam, I was summoned to speak to the medical director. He was concerned about giving me my medical license because I was taking Prozac," reports another doctor. "I don't know how he accessed my medical record."

Mental health questions on job applications are more than just an invasion of privacy. These questions are against the law. The ADA clearly states it is illegal to ask applicants disability-related questions. Yet physicians must answer these questions on insurance credentialing, state board licensing, and employment applications. Mental health questions are grouped with questions on criminality (such as felonies and DUIs) implying that a doctor who seeks mental health support is a criminal, further stigmatizing those who need psychological support—not punishment.

"In every job that I have applied for, as part of the credentialing process, there are questions about felonies, treatment for drug/alcohol abuse and mental illness," writes one physician. "Why are mental health questions still allowed to be on there? I have had postpartum anxiety/depression three times now and I feel like it is none of their damn business. So I have lied about it on my applications. Also, I feel these questions could contribute to doctors not seeking help, especially for serious problems that could require a mental health hospitalization. Do these questions have an adverse effect on doctors and medical students presenting (or not) for care they may desperately need?"

Yes, they do.

Five Reasons Doctors Don't Seek Mental Health Care

1. Doctors may be required to turn over their "confidential" medical records to others who invade their privacy and control their careers. Reference Confidentiality Breach for details.

2. State medical boards demand to read doctors' mental health records and may exclude physicians from practicing medicine in a particular state.

3. Hospitals demand to read doctors' mental health records and may exclude physicians from hospital staff privileges.

4. Insurance plans demand to read doctors' mental health records and may exclude physicians from insurance contracts.

5. Doctors with mental health conditions may be forced into costly, ineffective, and punitive PHPs (Physician Health Programs) in which they must submit to a 12-step program with random urine drug screens—even if they have never used drugs. (Note: PHPs have been effective for some physicians with substance abuse.) Reference No Mental Heath Care for more details.

Illegal mental health questions have remained unchallenged far too long and have had a detrimental effect on doctors and medical students who delay and avoid needed care.

Fear of seeking treatment due to these antiquated, punitive, and illegal questions leads to increased physician depression, anxiety, substance abuse, and suicide. I know of many medical students and physicians who died by suicide for fear of seeking mental health care that would be disclosed on their official school records, residency applications, hospital privileges, state licensure, and insurance credentialing.

Physicians' mental health needs are too often met with punishment or neglect. One doctor reports: "When I was a fourth-year medical student at Ohio State, my lab partner suicided. We had a five-minute meeting. Then back to the wards. I started crying on the wards. The team looked at me as if I were crazy. I went to the nurses' lounge where a medical assistant prayed with me. I went back about thirty minutes later. I was not excused for the day."

We enter medicine with our mental health on par with or better than our peers, yet anxiety, depression, and suicide are occupational hazards of our profession. We are chronically exposed to human suffering and death, yet offered no on-the-job emotional support. Instead, we're punished if we seek mental health care—even if we need to grieve the suicide of a colleague for more than five minutes. How can we care for others if we can't get the care we need as human beings—without fear, stigma, and discrimination?

It's time to end the physician mental health witch hunt. Seeking psychological support should be encouraged, not punished. I believe all medical students and doctors require confidential mental health care to be well-adjusted human beings. We should be far more concerned about physicians who don't receive mental health care.

TAKE ACTION NOW

1. Get regular confidential mental health care during your medical education and career. Skilled mental health professionals can treat you without compromising your confidentiality. Many use paper charts, do not input into an electronic medical record, and will even offer same-day virtual sessions 24/7 that you can access from the comfort of your home.

2. Let your medical institution know that you have a mental health disability and need accommodations. Legally they must know that you have a disability before they will be held liable for discrimination. According to the EEOC (Equal Employment Opportunity Commission) employers must provide reasonable accommodation for a mental health disability of a qualified employee or applicant.

3. File an official disability discrimination complaint with your employer (and maintain a copy of that complaint with date stamp). Your employer must investigate formal complaints of discrimination in the workplace.

4. Do not depend on in-house protection of your rights. If your employer fails to act in a timely manner, you may also file a complaint of employment discrimination at your local EEOC. They will investigate your case and when it is complete you may request a hearing before an EEOC judge.

5. Demand that your state board, hospital, and insurance plans remove mental health questions from applications. Some states already have. Invasive "Have-you-ever-had" questions should at minimum be replaced with "Do you currently have any condition that would impair your ability to safely practice medicine?" **Mental illness does not equal impairment.**

6. If you are distressed and need to talk to someone now, please contact me at IdealMedicalCare.org.

7. To proceed with legal action, contact an attorney skilled in disability discrimination who will file a lawsuit in federal district court.

8. Document all discrimination related to mental health disability directed at you or any other medical professional. Include evidence in the form of statements related to adverse actions taken against you or others due to a mental health conditions. Reference <u>Human Rights Violations Documentation Guidelines</u>.

Document Mental Health Disability Discrimination

_____

_____

_____

_____

_____

_____

_____

_____

_____

_____

_____

_____

_____

_____

_____

_____

_____

Discrimination, Physical Disability

*Mistreatment by a medical institution/employer of a
medical professional with a physical disability protected
by anti-discrimination law.*

The Universal Declaration of Human Rights, Article 2, proclaims: "Everyone is entitled to all the rights and freedoms set forth in this Declaration, without distinction of any kind, such as race, color, sex, language, religion, political or other opinion, national or social origin, property, birth or other status."

Our United States Civil Rights Act of 1964, Title VII, also declares: "It shall be an unlawful employment practice for an employer to fail or refuse to hire or to discharge any individual, or otherwise to discriminate against any individual with respect to compensation, terms, conditions, or privileges of employment, because of such individual's race, color, religion, sex, or national origin."

Expanding upon the Civil Rights Act is the Americans with Disabilities Act of 1990 that states: "No covered entity shall discriminate against a qualified individual on the basis of disability in regard to job application procedures, the hiring, advancement, or discharge of employees, employee compensation, job training, and other terms, conditions, and privileges of employment."

Surprisingly, health care facilities and medical schools discriminate and retaliate against their students and physicians with physical disabilities—a practice completely opposed to their stated healing mission of providing compassionate medical care. Sadly, our own medical institutions fail to comply with the Americans with Disabilities Act, the United States Civil Rights Act, and the Universal Declaration of Human Rights.

Medical students and physicians continue to report being victimized by medical institutions for having migraines, diabetes, and cancer.

"Dr. Wible, I was dismissed from medical school in the beginning of my fourth year because I had a medical condition [migraines] that didn't help the school's 'technical standards.' I suffered abuse my entire third year from residents and physicians telling me that I wasn't fit to be in medicine, that if I knew what was good for me I would just drop out," reports one woman. "My school told me that being sick was akin to being unprofessional, and that I should give up my dreams of wanting to become a physician. They pulled me into their administrative office several times to harass me, and eventually told me that I was dismissed."

"I was fired for needing a wheelchair or walker after hip surgery," reports another physician.

Sometimes victims use the terms harassment and discrimination interchangeably. Yet workplace harassment is only unlawful when an employee is treated poorly (often name calling or unwanted touching) because of a protected characteristic or activity, and discrimination is when an employer takes an *adverse action* such as termination against an employee because of a protected characteristic. Harassment and discrimination can both be unlawful. Workplace harassment and discrimination can sometimes lead to such desperation in medical professionals that they end their lives by suicide.

Does a resident physician have a right to be a doctor and a patient? Not according to one prestigious United States hospital that obstructed a young psychiatry resident from receiving life-saving intervention for her newly diagnosed kidney cancer.

"My program had been punishing me and accusing me of being 'unprofessional' for attending appointments. When I began standing up for my basic human right to life-saving medical care, I was repeatedly retaliated against. This retaliation occurred even after I pointed out the fact that my doctor told me had I not received the treatment they punished me for, I would not likely be alive today. That fact did not appear to register with my superiors. I then went to the dean's office, then to the ombudsman, then to the institution's president. They ignored me. So I decided to go outside of the institution. That surely got their attention as not even a month after going to the government I received an email from my institution stating there was a vote for my termination. At least they stopped ignoring me. I had documentation of what I had been through since my diagnosis and proof that my performance was at or above average. Despite major surgery, tubes, drains, fainting, vomiting, and panic attacks, I was still able to be a good doctor. I always put the safety of my patients first and I don't think there is anyone in this world who can contest that, not even those who voted for my termination. Next week I am scheduled to have an MRI and I do not know if I will have a paycheck or even health insurance to cover it."

Serious human rights violations continue to be inflicted upon our doctors with physical disabilities—often occupationally induced or accelerated by unsafe working conditions. If you have suffered from disability discrimination, take action and acquire legal counsel.

TAKE ACTION NOW

1. Let your medical institution know that you have a physical disability and need accommodations. Legally they must know that you have a disability before they will be held liable for discrimination. According to the EEOC (Equal Employment Opportunity Commission) employers must provide reasonable accommodation for a physical disability of a qualified employee or applicant.

2. File an official disability discrimination complaint with your employer (and maintain a copy of that complaint with date stamp). Your employer must investigate formal complaints of discrimination in the workplace.

3. Do not depend on in-house protection of your rights. If your employer fails to act in a timely manner, you may also file a complaint of employment discrimination at your local EEOC. They will investigate your case and when it is complete you may request a hearing before an EEOC judge.

4. Contact an attorney skilled in disability discrimination who will file a lawsuit in federal district court.

5. Document all discrimination related to physical disability directed at you or any other medical professional. Include evidence in the form of statements related to adverse actions taken against you or others due to a physical medical conditions. Reference <u>Human Rights Violations Documentation Guidelines</u>.

Document Physical Health Disability Discrimination

_____

_____

_____

_____

_____

_____

_____

_____

_____

_____

_____

_____

_____

_____

_____

_____

_____

_____

_____

_____

_____

Discrimination, Racial

Mistreatment by a medical institution/employer of a medical professional based upon race protected by anti-discrimination law.

The Universal Declaration of Human Rights, Article 2, proclaims: "Everyone is entitled to all the rights and freedoms set forth in this Declaration, without distinction of any kind, such as race, color, sex, language, religion, political or other opinion, national or social origin, property, birth or other status."

Our United States Civil Rights Act of 1964, Title VII, also declares: "It shall be an unlawful employment practice for an employer to fail or refuse to hire or to discharge any individual, or otherwise to discriminate against any individual with respect to compensation, terms, conditions, or privileges of employment, because of such individual's race, color, religion, sex, or national origin."

Racial discrimination persists in medical training and begins even during medical school and residency interviews.

"When I applied for residency, two places said they are not looking for black residents," shares one doctor. Another says, "An attending asked if I was one of those affirmative action cases. I am black and a woman."

"My wife applied to a historically black medical school. They told her at the interview that she would not be accepted because she was white and they assumed that, if accepted, she'd attempt to transfer out as soon as possible."

"As an attending physician, I enter a patient hospital room and the parent asks if I'm there to take their food order," states an African-American female physician. "I am dressed in my white coat, hospital ID badge with my stethoscope around my neck. While other physicians are free to wear their regular clothing at work, you will always find me in my white coat lest I be confused with the dietary team."

Darker-skinned female physicians are often demoted by patients and staff who view them as nonphysicians.

"I am an African-American woman and it was incredibly clear other doctors did not view me as a colleague. I even had psychiatry called on me when I kept insisting I was a medical doctor. Sad." Sending doctors who defend themselves against discrimination for mandatory psychiatric evaluation is a tactic used by medical institutions to label victims intolerant of injustice with "mental illness" on their permanent professional record in an attempt to undermine their careers. Reference Forced Drugging for details.

Racial discrimination is dehumanizing for medical trainees, particularly when they witness teachers mistreat patients based solely on skin color. Some attendings have refused to care for dark-skinned patients and provided lesser resuscitation efforts for Latino and African-American newborns. "I have heard multiple attendings say, "These are illegals. Why are they here at this hospital? They don't deserve our care.""

Institutional racial discrimination is made visible in a lack of departmental diversity. Cafeteria staff are predominantly dark-skinned women while hallways are lined with massive oil paintings of old white guys. A display of racial privilege and power for all who walk through the hospital.

"Our state university med school administrator decided to 'reorganize' a big clinical department in a manner that would eliminate numerous positions (mostly division chiefs)," reports one doctor. "Institutional policy required that unit reorganizations resulting in job losses first must be set forth in a written plan. That plan is then subject to multiple levels of review and approval, specifically including review for potential discriminatory impact by the university Equity and Diversity Office. None of these policy steps were followed. The departmental reorganization reduced the proportion of minorities holding the affected positions from 40 percent of the total number of positions to zero. A minority faculty member whose job had been affected by the reorganization filed a discrimination complaint, pointing to the disparate impact of the reorganization on minorities. A collateral discrimination complaint was filed by a different faculty member, alleging that the administrator in question had, in a faculty meeting, boastfully analogized his leadership style to that of Nazi Germany. Despite the fact that mathematically there can be no greater 'disparate impact' than reducing minority representation to zero, the complaint was rejected as being supported by 'no evidence.' The complaint involving the Nazi analogy was likewise rejected after the administrator (who admitted to making the comment) said that his words had been misunderstood."

Even with dramatic cases of racial discrimination in our hospitals, our own medical institutions tasked with protecting human health often look the other way.

TAKE ACTION NOW

1. File an official complaint with your employer (and maintain a copy of that complaint with date stamp). Your employer must investigate and act on formal complaints of discrimination in the workplace.

2. Do not depend on in-house protection of your rights. If your employer fails to act or resolve the issue in a timely manner, you may also file a complaint of employment discrimination at your local EEOC (Equal Employment Opportunity Commission). They will investigate your case and when it is complete you may request a hearing before an EEOC judge.

3. Contact an attorney who will file a racial discrimination lawsuit in federal district court.

4. Document all racial discrimination at your medical institution. Encourage others to do the same. Uniting with victims strengthens your case. Reference <u>Human Rights Violations Documentation Guidelines</u>.

Document Racial Discrimination

Discrimination, Sexual

Mistreatment by a medical institution/employer of a medical professional based upon gender protected by anti-discrimination law.

The Universal Declaration of Human Rights, Article 2, proclaims: "Everyone is entitled to all the rights and freedoms set forth in this Declaration, without distinction of any kind, such as race, color, sex, language, religion, political or other opinion, national or social origin, property, birth or other status."

Our United States Civil Rights Act of 1964, Title VII, also declares: "It shall be an unlawful employment practice for an employer to fail or refuse to hire or to discharge any individual, or otherwise to discriminate against any individual with respect to compensation, terms, conditions, or privileges of employment, because of such individual's race, color, religion, sex, or national origin."

Though anyone can be the victim of sexual discrimination, women are the most common victims of pay disparity and have fewer opportunities for promotion. Women are more likely to be terminated when compared to men who are often protected by each other despite serious behavior issues. A friend reports: "My former chief had problems with cocaine use and was having sex with multiple nursing staff and residents. He was allowed to go through rehab and graduate."

Women in medicine earn less than men—even when they do more work. A female physician reports her first job's salary was $20,000 lower than a male classmate's employed in an identical position. Another woman shares the following: "I have made much less than male colleagues at the state hospital and I've worked with a much larger patient load for three decades now. I filed a complaint 15 years ago and was told the sample size is too small to make comparisons. I left to work for a private hospital for four years. I was on call twice as much as male physicians (as was my female colleague), sexually harassed by an administrator, and my office was moved to a former storage closet with no heat or air. Male physicians had large corner offices with windows. I was repeatedly told to do their work when they were too busy. I was continually harassed to submit fraudulent billing. Our significant pay disparity is not due to raising children, it is due to clear bias against women in medicine."

One reason women are paid less is because they are given excess scutwork, more complex cases, lower-reimbursing patients, and some are told to expect more Medicaid and charity cases because they're single and childless. Female physicians are often expected to work for free.

"Just signed on with a large organization and was required to do more than 30 hours of computer training and other modules on my own time," explains one female physician. "I was told all physicians did this on their own time and it was a 'company policy.' I know a male physician who had his training compensated. When the question was posed to the hiring manager, a white male, he said his final answer was 'no' and that he had started to have 'red flags' wondering if I was the right fit if I was going to pursue this."

TAKE ACTION NOW

1. File an official complaint with your employer (and maintain a copy of that complaint with date stamp). Your employer must investigate and act on formal complaints of sexual discrimination in the workplace.

2. Do not depend on in-house protection of your rights. If your employer fails to act or resolve the issue in a timely manner, you may also file a complaint of employment discrimination at your local EEOC (Equal Employment Opportunity Commission). They will investigate your case and when it is complete you may request a hearing before an EEOC judge.

3. Contact an attorney who will file a sexual discrimination lawsuit in federal district court.

4. Document all sexual discrimination in your medical institution. Encourage others to do the same. Uniting with victims strengthens your case. Reference Human Rights Violations Documentation Guidelines.

Document Sexual Discrimination

_____

_____

_____

_____

_____

_____

_____

_____

_____

_____

_____

_____

_____

_____

_____

_____

_____

_____

_____

_____

_____

_____

_____

Exploitation

*Profiteering or benefiting from the mistreatment
or abuse of a medical student or physician.*

Students enter medicine with a dream to heal others. However, they lack true informed consent of the financial, physical, and mental health risks of medical training. Article 26 of the Universal Declaration of Human Rights proclaims: "Education shall be directed to the full development of the human personality and to the strengthening of respect for human rights and fundamental freedoms." Yet enthusiastic naive students are often met by short-term profiteers who do not have their best interests at heart. Unaware of rampant human rights violations in medicine, they find themselves in situations that are overwhelming and scary. Disillusioned, depressed, and debt-ridden, they rightly feel exploited for their dreams—and may become suicidal.

"The decision to go to medical school was wrong. The idea that I could use the talents I have been blessed with to make a difference was a sham," explains one physician. "I am called obscene names on satisfaction surveys by patients for not filling their prescriptions for narcotics/tranquilizers/amphetamines; called to task by supervisors for my arrogance at adhering to medical standards of care; and drowning in debt I can't escape by bankruptcy. I am in the process of stacking my life insurance to adequately care for my wife and children. I know how and where. Knowing I am not alone does not change things."

An internal medicine resident who died by suicide writes in his final note, "I guess we all know that I chose the wrong field. I actually think it would've been a good fit for me a few decades ago, but I don't like what it is currently. Like every damn field in the world right now it appears that profit is the driving motive and things will continue to get worse as more profit is extracted. Now I'm left with a job I can barely stand and a mountain of debt (which FYI should be absolved upon my death)." He was never suicidal before medical school.

Though United States medical schools have an attrition rate of less than two percent, offshore for-profit medical schools with lax admission requirements combine high tuition with high acceptance and attrition rates, dumping more than 50 percent of their students before third year in a business model that exploits the dreams of humanitarians.

"I imagine all med schools are difficult," reports one student. "But mine is sadistic (a direct quote from our school counselor). My school is notorious for failing students—up to 20 percent of every class every semester. It doesn't matter if your brother just died, if you're 0.01 percent away from passing any class, you're dismissed. No makeup tests. Before med school, I was a 3.98 student. Today I'm a C+. Talk about deflating. I've gone to every department to figure out how to bring my grades up, but the response is, 'You're not smart enough.' I know that's not true, but it hurts that my school doesn't think I belong here (but they're happy to take my money). All this crap has culminated in a deep depression. I've developed test anxiety that paralyzes me during exams. The only help I've received is antidepressants. I constantly doubt myself. I even struggle to interact with my husband and son. I feel like an idiot for coming here—and even worse for dragging my family into this $200,000 mess without knowing if I'll ever pay it off. I worry that I'll never be able to practice medicine. It's enough to drive anyone mad."

After medical school, the exploitation continues in residency, as these physicians explain:

"Once we're in residency, what feels like indentured servitude begins. We can't really choose where we go. We can list the places we'd be willing to go, and a computer decides for us. We can't negotiate our contracts. We are frequently seen and treated by patients, other medical personnel, and (worst) our attending physicians as unwelcomed intruders. Attending physicians who feel that it's their right to treat residents like scum exist, and if you are unlucky enough to have one choose you as his/her pet destruction project, you have just bought into three to seven years of abject torture from someone who can literally end your entire career in a moment."

"Exploitative tactics are often mimicked by senior residents against their junior brethren to show off their toughness," reports another physician. "When the Joint Commission comes in, everyone is told to feed them the company line that, 'All is great at this wonderful institution.' Fear of further retribution is real if anything else is said. It's no wonder that young graduates are often broke, broken, addicted, divorced and even suicidal. Many unfortunately don't make it to graduation."

Residents often work 80 to 100 hours per week, earning less than minimum wage, while chronically exposed to suffering and death without proper supervision, support, or protection by labor laws. Scary for new doctors.

After residency, exploitation continues for physicians employed by corporations that take up to 85 percent of their revenue generation as overhead while forcing doctors to practice assembly-line medicine and commit insurance fraud by upcoding and billing for care they did not provide.

If medical students or physicians experience mental health issues amid the years of exploitation, they may be mandated to receive treatment at a physician health program at their own expense where their license will be held hostage unless they submit to a 12-step program and random urine drug screens (even though they don't have drug problems). Physician health programs profit from emotionally vulnerable physicians locked into contracts for up to five years. If doctors don't comply, they lose their medical license.

TAKE ACTION NOW

1. Be fully informed of all financial, psychological, and physical risks and benefits of a medical education and career. Google my keynote: "Secrets to loving your life in healthcare" for the inside scoop.

2. Avoid exploitation by medical schools that do not have your best interests at heart. Do your research. Get statistics. Explore medical school reviews. Check out private chatrooms and news forums like Reddit.

3. Choose your specialty carefully. Ensure you select your career path with informed consent from trusted mentors.

4. You must have at least one mentor in medicine who you meet with regularly for guidance and support.

5. Consider launching your own clinic and keeping the revenue you generate as a physician business owner or entrepreneur rather than being a physician employee. Google my keynote: "Beating physician 'burnout:' finding your bliss" for instructions.

6. Please do not end your life. If you are feeling disillusioned, contact me at IdealMedicalCare.org.

7. If you are overwhelmed by debt, you can get loan forgiveness even in a non-medical career. Your loans can be forgiven by starting your own nonprofit. You have more choices than you can imagine.

8. Document all exploitation. Never sign contracts that violate your human rights. Have all contracts reviewed by a lawyer. Even if you've agreed to exploitive terms, your documentation may assist you with a future legal case. Reference <u>Human Rights Violations Documentation Guidelines</u>.

Document Exploitation

_____

_____

_____

_____

_____

_____

_____

_____

Food Deprivation

Lack of access to food essential for normal function
of the human body of a medical professional.

The right to food is protected by Article 25 of the Universal Declaration of Human Rights. Medical professionals are well aware of the impact of food deprivation on the human body. When our physiologic needs for caloric input are unmet, the body struggles to function.

As a third-year medical student witnessing a surgery, I wasn't doing anything too important other than holding a retractor with another classmate. Suddenly she collapsed onto the floor. She was out. Her blood sugar was 26. They checked my blood sugar. It was 24. I was still standing. In fact, I made it through medical school on organic carrots, kale, lentil soup, and no caffeine. I was super pure then. However, even if caloric restriction increases longevity, surviving medical training with a blood sugar of 24 isn't healthy.

Yet hypoglycemia is common among medical trainees who have no time to eat and are deprived of adequate calories to maintain body functions required for thinking properly and standing upright—important when assisting during surgery or making life-and-death decisions for vulnerable patients.

It's not uncommon to see medical students and residents fainting from hypoglycemia and recovering on gurneys in the hallway. A physician friend reports, "Two times I fainted from hypoglycemia. The second time I hit my head on a stretcher on the way down and I was given juice by a kind nurse and then expected to keep seeing patients like nothing happened."

"At my old residency, one resident went into diabetic ketoacidosis and required hospitalization for several days because of our irregular access to food and water," reports a physician.

Labor laws guarantee that employees get bathroom breaks and regular meals during their shifts. At my local PetSmart, my dog groomer gets two 15-minute paid breaks and one 30-minute unpaid break during her 8-hour shift. At my local Starbucks, baristas get two 10-minute paid breaks and one 30-minute unpaid break per 8-hour shift. Both work 40-hour work weeks. Even my pilot gets breaks and can't fly more than nine hours straight. Yet new doctors-in-training work 28 (or more) hours per shift without breaks, meals, or sleep and are expected to work 80 (or more) hours per week.

Labor laws don't apply to medical students, residents, or physicians. No bathroom breaks. No time for meals or snacks.

Due to irregular access to food on shifts that exceed 24 hours, medical students and physicians, like most victims of starvation, develop pathologic behaviors around food including stealing apple juice and crackers from the nurses' station or grabbing leftovers from patient trays. "I learned to eat fast," says one physician. "If you ever see someone eating fast they either served time in prison or medical residency!"

Doctors tend to multitask by combining emergency bowel-and-bladder-bursting bathroom breaks with meals. "Getting a break was sitting on the toilet doing your business while wolfing down anything!" shares another doctor.

"The cafeteria closed at 1:00 pm so usually we'd miss breakfast because we're on the wards at 7:00 am and breakfast is at 7:00. And then we'd often miss lunch because it is really hard to get off at 12:00 pm to go get something to eat," reports a hospitalist on multi-day shifts. "And then the cafeteria was closed because it's a small hospital so we'd have no access to food. And then I'd think, 'Well, I'm gonna go out to get a Whataburger, (which I hate eating) and then I wouldn't get out.' When we'd ask, 'Could we have access to food?' Administration would respond, 'Well, you outsiders, you come in and you tell us how you need to eat.' It was insane."

"I couldn't afford to buy food at the hospital on an inpatient medicine rotation," reports a trainee. "I also was given no place to store anything so I would fill my pockets with dollar store granola bars and pray they kept my stomach from growling. One day I forgot them and got so hungry after a long day that I stole cold leftover rice from a meal left for attendings in the physician's lounge. I was so afraid I would be caught and have to explain. I lost almost ten pounds off an already small frame during that rotation."

Medical trainees lose significant weight due to lack of access to food. A close physician friend went from 130 down to 88 pounds during the first five months of her intern year.

<u>TAKE ACTION NOW</u>

1. Request from your employer a copy of the workplace labor laws governing your right to have breaks and meals. If there are no guidelines for physicians, unite with your colleagues and petition for a safe working environment that protects medical professionals from life-threatening conditions that may impair our ability to safely care for patients.

2. Defend your right to eat when you are hungry. Never skip meals. When you have the chance to eat, please eat.

3. Carry plenty of snacks for yourself and colleagues who may be starving.

4. Sometimes self-neglect becomes so habituated you no longer track what and when you are eating. Keep a journal below. You might be surprised how dysfunctional your eating habits are—especially at work.

5. Document all episodes of food deprivation that endanger the lives of medical professionals or their patients. Reference <u>Human Rights Violations Documentation Guidelines</u>.

Document Food Deprivation

Forced Drugging

*Medication (usually psychotropics) forced upon a physician
or medical student under duress as a requirement
of employment or education.*

A form of retaliation, forced psychiatric evaluation and medication management are used to control or manipulate the behaviors and thoughts of individuals who challenge those in power.

I became aware of this practice when new interns would tell me the repercussions of correctly documenting their actual hours worked per week on official time logs, often in excess of the "80-hour cap." These conscientious new doctors who took pride in providing thorough medical care were then swiftly called into the program director's office each week and cited for committing duty-hour violations. Blamed like a criminal for committing a violation, they were labeled as "inefficient." If these overworked doctors continued to correctly document their work hours, they would be scheduled for psychiatric assessment and prescribed stimulant medication to force "compliance with the 80-hour cap." Of course, many new doctors avoided further confrontation by simply falsifying their work hours. Reference Lying.

After the suicide of a resident who was wrongfully terminated in the opinion of his peers, his surviving colleagues began to ask questions. Forced psychiatric assessment was used to censor and intimidate physicians:

"Several months before graduation, a pediatric resident at Duke took his life. It was a horrible tragedy that had a profound impact on the psyche of all of us residents. Unfortunately, we were completely silenced and the whole tragedy was swept under the rug. I was speaking with two resident colleagues after the incident and said, 'Something isn't right here.' Within thirty minutes I was called into my program director's office. There were four doctor administrators sitting behind a desk with legal pads and pens. They demanded that I sit down and share anything on my mind as they furiously scribbled notes. Tears streamed down my face and their cold stares persisted as they took notes. I can barely remember what happened because I was so scared and their intimidation and bullying tactics paralyzed me. The end result: I was immediately forced to go to psychiatric services to be 'cleared' so I could report back to clinic that same day and finish seeing patients. I thought I moved on but these visions still haunt me, years later. Some memories can never be erased and linger on in your soul."

Another resident shares, "Since starting medical school I have known one neurosurgery resident that died in a car crash due to fatigue, one of my former classmates died from an overdose of fentanyl, a resident at a hospital I rotated at died by suicide by leaping off the parking structure, and, just a few weeks ago a resident at the hospital where my wife works died by suicide by gunshot wound. Reading your article was like cold water in my face, particularly the following part. 'If they violate work hours (by caring for patients), they can be forced to lie on their time cards or be written up as inefficient and sent to a psychiatrist for stimulant medications.' I was a surgical resident who struggled with lack of sleep in a program which eventually was put on probation due to duty-hour violations, though we were bullied into lying about our hours. Any violations were our fault, not the program's. I was picked on by a more advanced resident, and the program director sent me to Employee Assistance Program because he thought I was the source of the problems. They sent me to a psychologist who diagnosed me with ADD. He sent me to a psychiatrist, who added bupropion and methylphenidate to my escitalopram. I ended up not having my contract renewed in the end."

Numerous cases of physician suicide on my registry reveal that physicians and trainees were placed on new psychiatric medications and not monitored properly in the weeks to months before their deaths. Many of these drugs have clear black-box warnings indicating risk of suicide. Reference Suicide.

TAKE ACTION NOW

1. Be wary when referred to a "preferred" psychiatrist by your employer or program director. Your confidential and protected health information may be breached. Reference <u>Confidentiality Breach</u>.

2. Elect to receive mental health care with your own psychiatrist who you choose (not one mandated by an employer).

3. Always ask the medical professional attending to your care (including those at Employee Assistance Programs) if indeed your records will be maintained in confidence. Remain alert as your medical records may be accessed by others at your institution with impure motives.

4. Never sign a contract with your employer or medical school that forces you to receive care at a preferred program that may breach your confidentiality or HIPAA rights.

5. Document all intimidation and retaliation by your medical institution that involves forced psychiatric care, new psychiatric diagnoses, new psychotropic medications. Always consult your own personal physician before making sudden changes to your treatment plan. Reference <u>Human Rights Violations Documentation Guidelines</u>.

Document Forced Drugging

_____

_____

_____

_____

_____

_____

_____

_____

Gaslighting

Psychological manipulation of a medical student or physician leading the victim to question their own sanity.

The goal of a gaslighter is to make a medical student or physician doubt themselves, lose their sense of identity, perception of reality, and self-worth. Article 26 of the Universal Declaration of Human Rights proclaims: "Education shall be directed to the full development of the human personality and to the strengthening of respect for human rights and fundamental freedoms." Yet gaslighting is a common form of manipulation and mind control in medicine—often through words and phrases that are repeated over and over again until victims are so worn down that they accept (and even defend these words) as their new reality. Gaslighting is psychological warfare.

Physician "burnout" is the most popular victim-blaming buzzword used to make medical professionals question their self-worth while distracting attention from the medical system that has perpetuated human rights violations on physicians. A slang word for end-stage drug addiction first used on the streets of inner city America in the early 1970s, "burnout" is now weirdly accepted as a real condition for doctors. Despite medicine's obsession with measuring physician "burnout" for nearly four decades, the epidemic of physician cynicism, exhaustion, and despair is worsening. Psychiatrists define "burnout" as a job-related dysphoria in an individual without major psychopathy—meaning you're normal; your job is killing you. You are not at fault. Stop accepting blame.

The proposed solution for physician "burnout" is physician resilience. The word resilience is used to blame doctors who are truly among the most resilient human beings on the planet and simply need to be treated with respect and supported in their work. If you made it into medical school you're already in the top one percent of compassion, intelligence, and resilience. You have no resilience deficiency. You are not defective. You are responding normally to an abusive medical system as this doctor explains:

"After a forced increase in work hours to maintain productivity, my chief publicly blew up at me unprovoked in the OR like something out of a horror movie as he morphed into a monster before my eyes and triggered my PTSD. Then the male physician administrator pats my hand, oozes sympathy, and honestly said, 'You are clearly the most burned out of our anesthesia group. Tell me how I can help you be more resilient.' I am a 61-year-old woman who has practiced anesthesiology for nearly 30 years: I am as bloody resilient as I can be! Why does the system create an untenable set of working conditions, causing stress and exhaustion, and when the predicted outcomes occur—I am the problem!"

To prevent physician "burnout," health care institutions may offer physician resilience workshops to train doctors to prioritize self-care and manage their emotions so they don't become disruptive—another term that blames doctors who express feelings of despair from gaslighting. Disruptive physicians who stand up and say no to abuse are then labeled as unprofessional. The list of gaslighting terms used to manipulate and confuse doctors are too numerous to compile (though I encourage you to keep your own list at the end of this chapter).

"Despite seeing a physician on a regular basis, I had to seek psychiatric evaluation at an emergency department," reports a trainee. "Rather than going to a facility covered by my insurance, my program insisted I come to my own hospital—what followed was an egregious violation of my health records that were modified and used against me. I was blamed for my mental health: my 'burnout' and my lack of 'resilience.' I was coerced into resignation, and I would later discover I was not the first nor the last resident in this program to experience this. I am still on the road to recovery from this harrowing experience."

The end result of using gaslighting words that blame doctors for the abuses committed by the medical-industrial complex is physician disempowerment, hopelessness, anxiety, depression—and suicide.

Appointing chief wellness officers to help physicians with "burnout" by mandating wellness modules for the abused can be part of the problem.

<u>TAKE ACTION NOW</u>

1. Always ask for precise definitions of all words used to blame doctors at your medical institution. If there is no definition or the meaning is so convoluted that you are confused, then there is a high probability the word is being used to gaslight you.

2. Ask, "What could I have done differently. What is the proposed solution?"

3. Talk to a trusted mentor to get feedback before accepting any label and definition as helpful to you.

4. Stop using gaslighting phrases like "physician burnout." Physicians are not the problem. Victims perpetuate the cycle of abuse by using the words of their oppressors.

5. Document, document, document. Save every email, record every conversation. If you are being blamed, manipulated, and confused at work, document everything. Reference <u>Human Rights Violations Documentation Guidelines</u>.

6. Keep a list of words used to blame doctors at your medical institution.

Gaslighting Words that Blame Doctors

Document Gaslighting

Harassment, Disability

Unwelcome or offensive conduct based upon a disability that creates a hostile work environment for a medical professional.

Unwelcome conduct based upon your mental or physical health is harassment and becomes unlawful when enduring the offensive conduct becomes a condition of employment, or the conduct is severe or pervasive enough to create a work environment that a reasonable person would consider intimidating, hostile, or abusive. Reference chapters on <u>Discrimination, Disability</u> and <u>Punishment when Sick</u> as there is overlap.

"My ex-boyfriend from medical school killed himself," reports one woman. "He got a coveted ortho residency. He had type 1 diabetes and his new attending told him he would never make it with diabetes. He shot himself a few days in."

Residents have been belittled for having brain tumors, miscarriages, cancer, depression—you name it. Physicians with depression are often told they are not happy enough and need to smile more—even in the aftermath of losing a colleague to suicide.

One medical school professor during the fourth week of class said, "If you ever feel depressed or overwhelmed, get out right now, you have no place in medicine. If you are feeling like that right now, there's the door."

In the aftermath of doctor suicides, departments have defamed the character of the deceased by spreading false accusations that the suicide victim had a "drug problem" or launching other personal attacks based on mental health conditions they developed during training. Posthumous harassment of a suicide victim by those who provoked the suicide is an outrage.

Tormenting medical students or doctors because of a mental or physical health condition (often occupationally induced) is harassment and should never be tolerated—especially within health care.

TAKE ACTION NOW

1. Read your medical institution's internal policies, including ACGME common core policies that prohibit disability harassment. Attach copies to your formal complaint.

2. Educate and inform those who may unintentionally (or intentionally) offend others by their words and actions. Request that disability harassment stop.

3. If the harassment limits your ability to participate in your medical education or care for patients and your medical institution has been alerted, they must take immediate action to investigate and eliminate the hostile environment. If they do not, proceed with legal action.

4. Unite and organize with other victims of disability harassment at your institution. Write down their personal contact information to keep in touch about your evolving case.

5. Hire a lawyer. As each case is unique, acquire legal counsel early to prevent career ramifications or ongoing abuse.

6. Identify, document, and confront mental and physical disability harassment in medical institutions. Record conversations. Take screenshots of harassment on medical institution social media pages. Reference Human Rights Violations Documentation Guidelines.

Document Disability Harassment

_____

_____

_____

_____

_____

_____

_____

_____

_____

_____

_____

_____

_____

_____

_____

_____

_____

_____

_____

_____

_____

_____

_____

_____

_____

_____

_____

_____

Harassment, Racial

*Unwelcome or offensive conduct based upon race that creates
a hostile work environment for a medical professional.*

Unwelcome conduct based upon race is harassment and becomes unlawful when enduring the offensive conduct becomes a condition of employment, or the conduct is severe or pervasive enough to create a work environment that a reasonable person would consider intimidating, hostile, or abusive. Reference Discrimination, Racial as there is some overlap.

Racial harassment in the workplace may take the form of microaggressions—everyday verbal and nonverbal mini-insults that may be intentional or unintentional. These comments are generally hostile or derogatory and target persons based solely upon their marginalized group.

One trainee reports, "I've heard many microaggressions against black patients from white doctors: 'You must be really good at basketball. You're really tall. How's your hoops?'"

"In Miami most everyone is Hispanic," reports a non-Spanish-speaking resident who explains, "I often found myself on rounds with my co-residents and attending having full conversations in Spanish and laughing without translating or including us non-Spanish speakers and, to be clear, this was not for the benefit of any patient nor one who did not speak English—all of them spoke English. They just chose to speak Spanish only."

"The white security guard at our medical school only asks dark-skinned students for their ID cards," reports one student.

Darker-skinned female physicians and medical students may be considered cleaning staff by patients who tell them to empty their bedpans. Some patients refuse to see African-American doctors and will hurl racial epithets such as, "I don't want no *n-word* doctor working on my baby." Patients in the South have even shown up for appointments wearing Confederate flag T-shirts.

"When my patients would say, 'Chinese have no souls, and we sure don't want a Chinese, soulless doctor,' I was told by my program that I had to get used to the disrespect and assume my racial inferiority or else I would be evaluated by psychiatry for having skin too thin to practice medicine."

"My great grandmother died. I was on call, crying. I was reprimanded and denied leave for the funeral. My chief resident called me a 'spic and tomato picker' loudly in front of the whole group. He said, 'Who else knows their great grandmother?' My program director (recently honored as Ohio Educator of the Year) said although I was called racial slurs, he would not intervene. Missing my great grandmother's funeral is a loss I feel on the anniversary of her death every year."

In India, senior doctors may harass juniors from other castes. Harassment has led to suicides. In contrast to suicide censorship in the United States, the suicide notes from Indian doctors are read on the evening news and arrests are made the same day. Suicide abetment is punished with up to ten years imprisonment.

Medicine is an apprenticeship profession. We learn how to be doctors by studying doctors. As medical trainees, we expect our teachers to protect and guide us along the path of becoming healers. Instead, some professors perpetuate racism and fail to protect trainees from racist patients and peers.

TAKE ACTION NOW

1. Read your medical institution's internal policies, including ACGME common core policies that prohibit harassment. Attach copies to your formal complaint.

2. Educate and inform those who may unintentionally (or intentionally) offend others by their words and actions. Request that harassment stop.

3. If the harassment limits your ability to participate in your medical education or care for patients, and your medical institution has been alerted, they must take immediate action to investigate and eliminate the hostile environment. If they do not, proceed with legal action.

4. Unite and organize with other victims of racial harassment at your institution. Write down their personal contact information to keep in touch about your evolving case.

5. Hire a lawyer. As each case is unique, acquire legal counsel early to prevent career ramifications from ongoing abuse.

6. Identify, document, and confront racial harassment in medical institutions. Record conversations. Take screenshots of harassment on medical institution social media pages. Reference Human Rights Violations Documentation Guidelines.

Document Racial Harassment

_____

_____

_____

_____

_____

_____

_____

_____

_____

_____

_____

_____

_____

_____

_____

_____

Harassment, Sexual

Unwelcome or offensive sexual conduct that creates a hostile work environment for a medical professional.

Unwelcome sexual conduct or comments is harassment and becomes unlawful when enduring the offensive conduct becomes a condition of employment, or the conduct is severe or pervasive enough to create a work environment that a reasonable person would consider intimidating, hostile, or abusive. Reference <u>Discrimination, Sexual</u>, as there is some overlap.

Though sexual harassment victims can be male or female, in a patriarchal medical system in which men predominate in power positions, the usual victims are female as outlined in a sampling of sexual harassment cases below:

"I have repeatedly had male supervising physicians (and sadly other women and nurses) comment on my breast size. I started wearing baggy clothes and then everyone kept asking if I was pregnant, even coming up to touch my abdomen. If I wore more fitted clothes, even with my white coat on, I was accused of being too sexy. My blonde hair and breast size seem to really fry people's brains. It's like they have no idea that I do have a brain! Meanwhile, nobody talks about whether male doctors wear ties or if their pants are too tight."

"I remember speaking to my mentor about my upcoming rotation with an esteemed neurologist. He told me, 'Oh, he's really going to like you!' I smiled thinking this was a compliment to my intellect, dedication, or work ethic. Then he added, 'He likes pretty girls.' He was right after all, as said neurologist later invited me out for wine."

"Female students were told we'd get a better evaluation on our orthopedic clinic rotation (with an older, male attending) if we wore lower-cut tops and pencil skirts, not slacks. Though off-putting, it was common knowledge for decades passed down from class to class."

Patients may even be outright sexually aggressive with female doctors, yet supervisors protect the offending patients and expect women to tolerate the abuse—often placing women directly in harm's way. One female medical student tells me she was sent in alone to remove suprapubic stitches on a man who had made sexual advances on her.

"I was a med student on a surgical rotation at a small hospital in Philly and I found myself alone in the doctors' lounge, with the chief of surgery. He knew I was considering applying for internship there. He cornered me (literally) and said he would make sure I got a spot if I'd give him oral sex. I managed to get out of the lounge. I finished the rotation, but was highly anxious. He threatened to fail me."

"When I showed the chair of psychiatry abusive emails from my chief resident, I was blamed. He said, 'Your co-residents think you are exotic.' He told me to change my glasses and wear my hair down and offer to bring coffee to the very same chief who had been harassing me. He did not hold them accountable for the abuse. I was expected to assume a female gender role to make the anger stop. This is the same mindset that expects women to protect themselves from rape by not going to parties rather than holding the rapists accountable. This conversation took place with other faculty present."

"When I became pregnant with my first child I was a chief resident. I went to a female attending for my first visit for my first pregnancy test. She immediately went to the chairman of the department and let him know I was pregnant and he called me into his office to berate me about it."

As a woman in medicine, I want to thank the men in our profession who speak out to stop the sexual harassment of women—often at their own expense. Male physicians submitted the following examples of advocacy and intervention on behalf of their peers:

"Where I went to residency, married male faculty were having sex with the female residents in the call rooms, and giving the male residents more call. One female resident attempted suicide over this due to the pressure. I blew the whistle to the dean over our program. I was thrown out of residency for 'going outside the residency.' Fifteen years later, they still give me a hard time and have allowed tampered education records to remain in my file because it was my fault for blowing the whistle."

"I would recommend the medical community look critically at the history of resident suicides in our internal medicine department. I got off lightly being a male. This church minister and man of God used to troll the pictures of female medical students for his internal medicine rotation. The most desirable one or two would be selected to go away with him to a conference. And if she didn't put out, she wouldn't get a good rating. He told one of the female residents, 'Your ass is too fat. Your husband will stop fucking you and get someone else.' He corrupted the entire residency process. I am certain that he wished me to suicide. What happened to him after ten years of being residency director? He went to an Ivy League medical school as dean of education. Talk about the perp shuffle."

TAKE ACTION NOW

1. Read your medical institution's internal policies, including ACGME common core policies that prohibit sexual harassment. Attach copies to your formal complaint.

2. Educate and inform those who may unintentionally (or intentionally) offend others by their words and actions. Request that sexual harassment stop.

3. If the sexual harassment limits your ability to participate in your medical education or care for patients, and your medical institution has been alerted, they must take immediate action to investigate and eliminate the hostile environment. If they do not, proceed with legal action.

4. Unite and organize with other victims of sexual harassment at your institution. Write down their personal contact information to keep in touch about your evolving case.

5. Hire a lawyer. As each case is unique, acquire legal counsel early to prevent career ramifications or ongoing abuse.

6. Identify, document, and confront sexual harassment in medical institutions. Record conversations. Take screenshots of harassment on medical institution social media pages. Reference Human Rights Violations Documentation Guidelines.

Document Sexual Harassment

_____

_____

_____

_____

_____

_____

_____

_____

_____

_____

_____

_____

_____

_____

_____

_____

_____

_____

_____

_____

Hazing

*Humiliating and dangerous rituals imposed upon
medical students and physician trainees as part
of their medical education.*

Medical initiation rites can range from benign pranks to serious chronic and repetitive patterns of behavior that are criminal. According to article 26 of the Universal Declaration of Human Rights proclaims: "Education shall be directed to the full development of the human personality and to the strengthening of respect for human rights and fundamental freedoms." Hazing is illegal in most states and prohibited by institutions such as colleges and universities due to health impacts from physical and psychological abuse.

The most common form of hazing in medical education is sleep deprivation. Extreme sleep deprivation makes victims more vulnerable to the negative impacts of other hazing rituals such as pranks with dead patients, forcing students who can't answer medical questions to do push-ups, compelled sexual activity, even physical assault. Of course, all hazing is supposed to make you a great doctor who can withstand any abusive working conditions in service of your patients.

"Sleep deprivation was devastating," according to one trainee, "and I have come to see it as completely counterproductive as an educational strategy. It risks countless patients' lives and serves only as an advanced form of hazing, more thorough and relentless and of greater duration than any hazing I've found elsewhere. Other forms of bullying take on new toxicity when one is so weakened and vulnerable."

I am frequently on the phone with residents and fellows (and sometimes their parents) who are concerned about the mental health impacts of extreme sleep deprivation leading to thoughts of suicide. Hazing may continue for more than a decade (surgery residencies may be seven years long on top of four years of medical school). One father called me about his brilliant suicidal son in a neurosurgery residency. He was only permitted to sleep three hours each night before performing unsupervised brain surgeries each day. Reference Sleep Deprivation for the dangers to trainees and patients.

During medical school, my classmates would play pranks with dead body parts from our anatomy lab. Very disrespectful to the corpse and also disturbing to the students—most of whom had never been around a dead human body. Pranks can become more vicious during clinical years and used as retaliation.

"I got a migraine with aura on newborn ICU call," shares one doctor. "I literally couldn't read the orders and had to call over my resident. I told her I had to lie down in the next ten minutes before the pain hit or I'd be unable to work later. Grumbling, they left me alone for a half hour. Then my resident returned and said, 'Examine this new one' and pulled me half asleep to a cold, turned-off open warmer with an unwrapped baby inside. He had gastroschisis [birth defect of abdominal wall in which baby's intestines are outside of the body], and I didn't in the first moment realize he had already died, since I wasn't given any history, just handed the form. My impression was only of his perfect and sweet smaller-than-term face, his ruined middle, and how he was blue and cold and too stiff, with amniotic banding on one arm and leg. After a second, I realized what had been done to me, and was horrified and tried hard not to cry. That was the only serious hazing I ever experienced."

Medical training has often been compared to a cult with an authoritarian leader in which submission is expected with no tolerance for questions. Abusive rituals are passed down from generation to generation and accepted as normal.

Stockholm syndrome is a condition in which victims develop empathy for their captors—even support their abusive rituals. Call attention to abuse and victims defend it because hazing makes great doctors. Doctors with Stockholm syndrome fight to maintain antiquated medical traditions rampant with human rights violations. They warn, "Let's not turn medicine into some coddling group hug where anyone with a brain can get through." And they state, "Physicians who complain about bullying and hazing are just spoiled brats and crybabies who are not cut out for a profession that has individual lives in the balance."

Doctors with Stockholm syndrome actually believe the newer generation of physicians is emotionally weaker and more likely to succumb to suicide. They truly believe that their abusive rituals will save us from future generations of lazy doctors. Please help them understand that hazing harms us all.

TAKE ACTION NOW

1. Research anti-hazing laws in your state and anti-hazing policies at your institution of higher education. Attach documentation to your complaint.

2. Unite with other hazing victims and petition your medical institution as a group to stop hazing activities.

3. Identify attendings and colleagues suffering from Stockholm syndrome. Having insight into what causes their behavior will help you end hazing at your institution. Knowledge is power.

4. Get legal counsel for guidance on the best course of action in cases of serious hazing.

5. Identify and document all hazing rituals at your medical institution. Reference Human Rights Violations Documentation Guidelines.

Document Hazing

_____

_____

_____

_____

Illegal Activity

Unlawful acts required of medical professionals to maintain employment or educational trajectory.

The list of illegal activities in medicine is so enormous it's challenging for me to know where to start. Most chapters in this book are human rights violations that are illegal under state or federal law and prohibited within policies at medical institutions. Yet illegal activity persists when victims and persecutors look the other way and ignore the sheer volume of unlawful behavior.

Common illegal activities in health care include performing and billing for unnecessary procedures, and withholding medical care to enrich for-profit insurance companies and other organizations that may provide personal financial gain for physicians. Other violations include overbilling and charging for services never performed, falsifying claims and diagnoses, prescribing unnecessary drugs to patients, lying to patients, lying in the medical record, falsifying work hour logs, and breaching confidentiality of patients' or colleagues' protected health information.

You may know doctors who participate in drug trafficking, sexual misconduct with patients, disability discrimination, racism, sexual harassment, and assault. You may have witnessed illegal activities in your career that have maimed, harmed, and killed vulnerable people. Some of those vulnerable people were medical students and residents and even beloved practicing physicians. Some of these people lost their careers. Some lost their lives to suicide. We are all harmed when illegal activities continue in our health care institutions. Illegal activity won't stop on its own. Our profession, our peers, our patients—and future generations of doctors—need your help to stop the cycle.

Hurt people hurt people. Wounded healers wound each other and their patients. This book is a call to action for all doctors and medical students of conscience to stop the cycle of abuse in medicine. Thank you for caring.

TAKE ACTION NOW

1. Review the chapters in this book and identify the specific illegal activities at your medical institution. Then take action. By not taking action, you are an accomplice to crimes against humanity—and you are breaking the oath that brought you to medicine in the first place.

2. If you are a perpetrator of illegal activity, stop now before you bring additional harm to yourself and others. Get help. Speak up. Assist other doctors who have participated in illegal schemes with you or others. You can stop the cycle of abuse in medicine.

3. If you are a victim of illegal activity in medicine, get help now. You can stop the cycle of abuse so that nobody else is ever victimized like you were.

4. Document all illegal activities at your medical institution, particularly if you were pressured to participate in unlawful acts or if patients were injured. Reference <u>Human Rights Violations Documentation Guidelines</u>.

Document Illegal Activity

_____

_____

_____

_____

Intimidation

Terrorizing medical trainees in the guise of medical education to maintain power and control over students and physicians-in-training.

Article 26 of the Universal Declaration of Human Rights proclaims: "Education shall be directed to the full development of the human personality and to the strengthening of respect for human rights and fundamental freedoms." Yet intimidation is a traditional teaching technique and often begins on day one of medical school as one retired surgeon recounts:

"I was happy, secure, and mostly unafraid until med school. I recall in vivid detail the first orientation day. Our anatomy professor stood before an auditorium filled with 125 eager, nervous, idealistic would-be healers and said these words: 'If you decide to commit suicide, do it right so you do not become a burden to society.' He then described in anatomical detail how to commit suicide. I have often wondered how many auditoriums full of new students heard those words from him. I am sure someone stood in front of us and told us what a wonderful and rewarding profession we had chosen. I do not remember those words. But I do remember how to successfully commit suicide—with a gun."

Students who are intimidated during their medical education are more likely to be stressed, depressed, suicidal—and to regret their career choice. I've been running a suicide helpline for medical students and physicians since 2012 and sadly, I've heard similar orientation horror stories from recent first-year medical students:

"The incoming class at my medical school was just told by our assistant dean of academic affairs on their first day of orientation that he was there to 'crush their souls.'"

At a Puerto Rican medical school, one professor welcomed students with, "You guys think you are so brilliant, but all you are, really, is a bunch of rejects from all other schools. That's what you are."

Another popular orientation speech goes something like this: "Look around the room to the student on your left and right. By the end of the year half of you won't be here."

"Dr. Wible, I'm at a medical school where the president of the school tells students daily to kill themselves, jump off the top of the building. He also personally attacks students based on weight." (This is ongoing at the time of publication.)

In a profession with a high suicide rate, encouraging students to kill themselves is not only cruel, it's punishable by law.

"An anatomy professor did inform us that we would commit suicide at a higher than average rate and told us from the lectern how to accomplish it successfully. I considered following the instructions on three occasions: once in my third year, once as an intern, and most recently when my four-year-old patient died."

Professors use public intimidation for group control and submission to the dominant hierarchy. Yet intimidation creates a hostile environment. Students who fear their teachers are less engaged and have lower self-confidence. Terror-based training has no place in modern medical education. Yet those who have been taught by terror are now in teaching positions continuing the cycle.

"A female surgeon told a resident who had made an error that what he did was so bad he should go home and kill himself in a text which is still being forwarded five years later!"

"I was told by a chief resident that if I didn't like how things were run that I should 'kill myself.' Then the program director told me: 'You're going to have to take a few beatings.' There's a difference between being tough and outright abuse."

Most trainees who experience intimidation in medical education rarely report their abuse to authorities who could help them. Many authorities who could intervene, don't help their trainees. To instill humanism into the next generation of physicians, we must stop wounding them.

TAKE ACTION NOW

1. Make copies of policy statements from your medical institution regarding bullying, hazing, and intimidation.

2. Unite with students to petition your institution to eradicate fear-based teaching methods. You are less likely to experience retaliation for protesting intimidation tactics if you do this as a group. Review <u>Bullying</u> for inspiration on how one medical school class removed a bully professor.

3. If you witness intimidation of a medical trainee, speak out. Comfort victims and help teachers stop the cycle of abuse.

4. Identify and document all instances of intimidation and terror-driven teaching at your medical institution (especially when instructions for suicide are given). All medical school orientations involving intimidation tactics should be captured by audio and video. Reference <u>Human Rights Violations Documentation Guidelines</u>.

Document Intimidation

_____

_____

_____

_____

_____

_____

_____

_____

J-1 Visa Abuse

*Human rights violations against foreign medical trainees
or physicians who risk deportation when they don't
submit to mistreatment.*

As if human rights abuse against medical residents is not overwhelming enough, one group fares even worse—foreign medical trainees who come to the United States often escaping economic and political turmoil with a dream for a better life. Most are on a visa (either J-1 or H-1). The requirements for various visas differ and are not the focus of this chapter dealing with general treatment of IMGs (International Medical Graduates), physicians who received their medical degrees outside the United States or Canada and require a visa for residency.

A dear friend explained to me her situation as a medical resident. Having landed in the United States from Romania in culture shock without complete fluency in English, she suddenly found herself "thrown to the wolves," working 36-hour shifts and 126-hour weeks in a New York City intensive care unit without adequate supervision. Despite extreme sleep deprivation and lack of food, time to bathe or even urinate, she was thankful to be here. She was working the equivalent of three full-time jobs and getting paid less than minimum wage, yet was grateful that her residency program was more humane than most.

Foreign trainees are at higher risk of exploitation by employers because they fear deportation if they don't submit to their job requirements. Employers and hospitals treat them poorly, knowing they are unlikely to acquire legal protection. After residency training, they are locked into multi-year requirements in underserved areas where they can't complain or they'll lose their employer-sponsored visa. One friend told me about a J-1 visa physician dangerously overworked at her hospital. He was so sleep deprived that he had a seizure in front of the hospital administrators and their response was to send him right back into the intensive care unit to treat the sickest patients with no oversight. As a hospitalist, he worked 168-hours—that's a full week in the hospital.

Foreign doctors risk being underpaid, mistreated, and trapped in jobs with employers who sponsor their visas. They are at higher risk of racial and sexual harassment and I'm aware of several cases of suicide among foreign doctors training in the United States.

TAKE ACTION NOW

1. Be aware of the unique pressures faced by foreign trainees and reach out to support them.

2. Speak up about abuse. If you are a United States citizen in medicine, your advocacy is crucial for medical trainees who do not enjoy the same support and protections you have.

3. Offer your phone number and contact information as an American medical professional to foreign trainees who have no family to turn to in the United States. Let them know that you care.

4. Report labor abuse against IMGs to the Department of State through the United States Citizenship and Immigration Services.

5. Seek legal counsel with an attorney skilled in representing foreign physicians and trainees.

6. Document all human rights violations against foreign medical trainees or physicians at your medical institution.

Document Abuse of International Medical Graduates

Joking

Humor that violates the humanity of patients,
medical students, or physicians.

Gallows humor makes fun of life-threatening situations involving human suffering and death—and is frequently used by medical professionals in emergency departments to cope with the inevitable tragedies they witness. Though I love slapstick (and I'm related to the Three Stooges) I've never been able to laugh at jokes about patients. I've always been offended by insulting medical acronyms and crude comments about death. I'm even more disgusted by crass locker-room talk and the way some physicians try to bond with me through emotionally detached one-liners or cynical jabs.

Article 26 of the Universal Declaration of Human Rights proclaims: "Education shall be directed to the full development of the human personality and to the strengthening of respect for human rights and fundamental freedoms." Yet hospital humor tends to objectify, dehumanize, and demean patients who are under our care while eroding the humanity of medical students and physicians who are obviously having trouble coping with emotionally distressing situations.

Patients would be horrified by hospital humor. Some have recordings of insults during surgery and they've won lawsuits as a result of their physician's foul jokes.

Yet proponents of this type of trauma humor believe it is a non-destructive and empowering coping mechanism that helps doctors bond amid tragedy. Is laughing at a patient's expense a doctor's only way to prevent tears? Maybe laughing during tragedy is an involuntary coping mechanism. The wife of a physician shares her husband's odd reaction to the loss of his medical school classmate:

"When my ex-husband was in medical school, his lab partner and friend (good buddy and mentor) drove out into a field one day and shot himself in the head. We found out about it on Halloween Eve. My husband started to laugh; the strangest hiccupping sound I ever heard came out of his mouth. He never laughed any other way after that; he seldom ever laughed after that. He too struggled with depression and suicidal thoughts, as well as alcoholism and sexual addiction/multiple affairs. We were married 21 years and then he divorced me for someone ten years younger. He is estranged from his daughters, weighs close to 400 pounds, and I seldom see him. When I do, I get an overwhelming feeling of sadness for the slow suicide that is his life, for the beautiful man who is missing in action forever. He was a musician, a poet, a gifted singer, writer, and gardener—none of which he does anymore."

The mother of a sleep-deprived surgery intern shared, "He told stories of how he and his partner on rotation fell asleep leaning against the walls while waiting for their patient's turn for a scan. He spoke of them as funny tales of residency." Seven weeks into surgery residency he died by suicide.

Though a transient laugh can briefly transform tragedy and boost spirits amid horror, I don't believe laughter and jokes are the ideal way to help medical professionals cope with trauma. Most people don't bond over codes, crash carts, and stillborns. Bonding over trauma creates trauma bonds—and trauma-bond humor—which is little more than institutionalized dehumanization of patients by dehumanized doctors.

What physicians really need is mental health care so they have a way to deal with their chronic exposure to incapacitating grief without psychologically dissociating and fragmenting their own humanity with offensive humor.

TAKE ACTION NOW

1. Think twice before saying something derogatory about a patient. Remember, physicians have had their statements recorded and aired in a court of law.

2. If you are a medical professional exposed to trauma and death, please seek professional counseling. Encourage your medical institution to offer on-the-job, non-punitive mental health care for all high-risk medical personnel as well as mandatory debriefing sessions after bad outcomes.

3. Be available to help physicians who habitually demean patients or resort to dehumanizing humor as their only coping mechanism for dealing with tragedy.

4. Document all instances of offensive humor at your medical institution below.

Document Offensive Jokes & Hospital Humor

_____

_____

_____

_____

_____

_____

_____

_____

_____

_____

_____

_____

_____

_____

_____

_____

_____

_____

Karōshi
Physician death by overwork.

Karojishi
Physician suicide by overwork.

The Universal Declaration of Human Rights, Articles 5, proclaims: "No one shall be subjected to torture or to cruel, inhuman or degrading treatment or punishment." And Article 24 declares: "Everyone has the right to rest and leisure, including reasonable limitation of working hours and periodic holidays with pay."

In Japan, being worked to death is actually in the dictionary. Karōshi is a word that literally means death by overwork.

In the United States, the OSHA (Occupational Safety and Health Act) protects workers from being killed or harmed at work. The law requires employers to provide employees with working conditions free of known dangers. The physician work environment is clearly in violation of the OSHA general duty clause at times. Higher-hazard industries such as hospitals and clinics with more than ten employees must record serious work-related injuries that require more than first aid on an OSHA form and post a summary of their yearlong illness/injury log in a place where workers can view it. You have a right to request full copies of the report from your employer.

Within eight hours after an employee death due to a work-related incident, employers must report the fatality to the OSHA. Within 24 hours after an employee's inpatient hospitalization, amputation, or loss of an eye, due to a work-related incident, employers must submit a report to OSHA. Employers must also record work-related incidents resulting in loss of consciousness, absence from work, restricted work, job transfer, as well as work-related cancer, chronic irreversible diseases, fractured bones or teeth, punctured eardrums, needlesticks, and contaminated cuts, lacerations, punctures, and scratches with potentially infectious material.

One doctor shares, "My best friend from medical school died a few years ago, 55 years old, excellent health, swam every day. Genius—musician, internist, bicycle designer. His death affected me deeply. Mother found him dead. Suicide? Who knows; I call it karōshi—I'm sure you're familiar with that, 'excessive work death.' I've already submitted my letter of resignation. In a few months I'll be off the RVU treadmill. I may still work a few months a year, but I won't be a slave anymore."

After nonstop consecutive 32-hour shifts, Dr. Zhang, a 30-year-old cardiologist, nearly died from acute karōshi after coughing up more than 4 pints of blood. Surgeon Dr. Liang Fuqun has been praised as a hero by millions online for performing nine surgeries while being injected with a painkiller for acute appendicitis "oozing pus" by the time he received his own surgery. Medicine glorifies overwork and self-neglect.

In the United States the medical industry is negligent in tracking doctor deaths and suicides by overwork. When medical institutions fail to report physician deaths within eight hours—*as required by OSHA*—it is a breach of institutional integrity, an active cover up, and an obstruction of justice.

Most karōshi deaths in Asia are due to strokes, heart attacks, or suicides (karojishi). In Japan, the "karōshi line" is defined as a 60-hour work week. This line dictates the threshold over which a wrongful death lawsuit may be filed for government compensation. That means if you are consistently working beyond 60 hours per week and you die, your family may get a payout.

Meanwhile, resident physicians in the United States are legally forced to work 80-hour work weeks—that's two full-time jobs! To make matters worse, in 2017 (despite public protest) ACGME nearly doubled first-year doctors' shifts from 16 to 28 hours.

Doctors across the globe from United States to China and India are also dying by karojishi—suicide due to overwork. One victim from India writes this letter to me:

"You don't know how thankful I am to you for writing that article on physician suicide. I really wanted to hug you after reading it. I had a really rough day, 130 outpatients and 60 emergency admissions in a 12-hour duty. I work as a final-year internal medicine resident in one of the busiest hospitals in India. It takes me five hours by flight to reach my home from my hospital. I have my wife and six-month-old son (whom I've been with for 15 days since his birth) at home. I work day in and out just to be with them once in three months. I don't see my colleagues smile, I hear my patients' misery every day. I smile and crack jokes even when I am sad so that I can bring some joy into my patients' sorrowful lives. I see deaths every day in ward. I don't know if you would believe me, but four deaths per day in a single ward of 40 beds overcrowded to 125 patients admitted at a time. Two patients on a bed, two lying together on the floor. Poverty, misery, and pain all around. I have declared 12 patients dead in a day during one of my duties. This profession demands too much from us. I have thought about giving up and suicide a thousand times—the misery is too much for me to see 12 people die in a day." Months after writing me, this doctor died by suicide—karojishi.

TAKE ACTION NOW

1. You have the right to a safe workplace. If unsafe, unhealthful, or hazardous: (a) file an OSHA complaint; (b) request the latest yearlong OSHA injury report to ensure your employer has reported all workplace deaths, and; (c) request a NIOSH evaluation. Reference Human Rights Violations Documentation Guidelines.

2. If you are a patient, ask how long your doctor has been on shift. Your doctor deserves to sleep. You deserve a well-rested doctor. Boycott hospitals that endanger the lives of doctors and patients.

3. Demand that the ACGME limit work hours to safe standards as in other industries—maximum 16-hour shifts and 60-hour work weeks.

4. Document all deaths/suicides of medical professionals who worked more than 60 hours per week. Submit suicides to IdealMedicalCare.org.

Document All Deaths & Suicides by Overwork

Lying

Perpetuating false statements that may endanger
medical professionals and their patients.

Most students arrive at medical school with a high degree of ethics and compassion. By the time they graduate many leave disillusioned and cynical. Exposure to dishonesty and deceit in the clinical years plays a huge role.

Medicine is an apprenticeship profession. We learn to be doctors by studying doctors. What happens to young enthusiastic learners when they witness lying in medicine and are encouraged—even threatened to lie themselves? They accept that lying is part of the culture of medicine and is actually required in order to make it through medical training.

I became aware of widespread lying forced upon new interns who would tell me the impact of correctly documenting the actual hours worked per week on official time logs, often in excess of the "80-hour cap." These conscientious new doctors who took pride in providing thorough medical care were then called into the program director's office each week and cited for committing duty-hour violations. Blamed like criminals for committing violations, they were labeled inefficient. If these overworked doctors continued to correctly document their work hours, they would be scheduled for psychiatric assessment and prescribed stimulant medication to force compliance with the ACGME 80-hour cap. Of course, many new doctors avoid further confrontation by falsifying their work hours. Reference <u>Forced Drugging</u> for more details.

"We all lied to ACGME," reports one resident. "We were taken into a room by the program director and told to lie that we had no work-hour violations."

Lying about work hours maintains the facade of compliance with the ACGME work-hour cap. New doctors quickly learn that telling the truth puts their residency at risk for loss of accreditation for duty-hour violations. Loss of program accreditation would adversely impact the career of the honest intern and all the residents in the program who depend on the intern's dishonesty. So lying is further justified to protect the entire community.

Some hospitals have gone beyond one-on-one intimidation to ensure community compliance—lying on work hours—while forcing physician trainees to work unlimited hours for minimum wage. Some hospital IT departments make it impossible for a doctor to input any number greater than 80 on their work log in the official hospital computer system. If a trainee enters a number higher than 80, the computer locks up and a red flag citing work-hour violations appears on the screen forcing the trainee to input a false number in compliance with graduate medical education standards.

Nobody wants a sleep-deprived and overworked doctor making life-and-death decisions about their medical care in the hospital, yet lying on hospital records creates an even more dangerous precedent.

Once a new doctor learns to lie on hospital computers, they learn lying is condoned even in patient medical records. An overworked doctor can suddenly get more work done in less time—by lying. In just a few seconds boxes can be checked that make it appear a more thorough set of questions or examinations were included during a patient visit. Doctors learn to document things that were never performed and submit fraudulent insurance claims to bill for them. Some hospitals incentivize lying for profit. Reference Corruption for further details.

When doctors are lying on medical records, then students learn to lie on medical records. When everyone is lying, then lying becomes usual and customary behavior in our hospitals and clinics. Clearly, none of this plays out well for patients.

TAKE ACTION NOW

1. Stop lying or risk being complicit in serious corruption. Doctors have been imprisoned and have died by suicide when trapped in criminal rings that started out with one "benign" lie. When you choose to stop lying or distorting, put your decision in writing.

2. Unite with other victims in medical training and practice to stop institutionalized deceit that harms us all.

3. Document all lies. Reference <u>Human Rights Violations Documentation Guidelines</u>.

Document Lying

_____

_____

_____

_____

_____

_____

_____

_____

_____

_____

_____

_____

_____

_____

_____

_____

_____

Maternal Deprivation

Lack of access to a mother in medical training, leading to adverse health sequelae in mother, child, or fetal death.

Maternal deprivation means depriving children time with their mothers—and depriving mothers time with their children. A psychiatry resident told me that she had only seen her infant daughter for six waking hours of her life during the first six months of her training. That's maternal deprivation.

"I entered medical school so very confident in myself and that was beaten out of me," reports one trainee. "I was repeatedly told I was stupid. I was threatened with being sent away [on a rotation] from my six-month-old without warning for the sake of medical school. Motherhood was not supposed to be a priority."

Maternal deprivation is a violation of our human right to procreate and have a family. Female physicians in their fifties who have sacrificed their fertile years to their profession often regret not having children. Physicians in their thirties and forties are just launching their careers after a decade or more of medical training, yet working two to three full-time jobs allows no time to date. So female trainees are racing to freeze their eggs in hopes of starting a family—one day.

All people have a right to create a family and maintain family relationships with time for raising their children. The Universal Declaration of Human Rights, Article16, proclaims: "Men and women of full age, without any limitation due to race, nationality or religion, have the right to marry and to found a family," and further declares "the family is the natural and fundamental group unit of society and is entitled to protection by society and the State." However, the human rights of physicians and medical students are routinely violated when it comes to procreation, childrearing, caring for sick children, or even attending funerals of family members.

"During my residency, I was forced to work Christmas Eve, four weeks after a cesarean section. I was on Darvocet in terrible pain and terrified of making a mistake on my 36-hour shift. Then I was reprimanded for trying to breast pump over lunch hour and had to stop four months after my child was born. When my great grandmother died I was denied leave for the funeral. I turned fifty this year and sometimes I think of all I missed with my kids and family."

Female medical trainees also suffer miscarriages due to inhumane working conditions and are given no time off to grieve or process the death of their child.

"I was a senior resident with a severe spinal headache, lying on lounge sofa, supervising junior residents, afraid to use any more leave. I was told to get up. I had cerclage for preterm labor, and my doctor recommended bed rest but told me he knew I probably couldn't do it as a resident. Residency director told me if I took leave, it would extend my graduation date, and that meant I probably couldn't get a job. I believed him and worked. My water broke in clinic. I gave birth to 21-week infant who died two hours after birth."

Please note that maternal deprivation leading to fetal death may be grounds for a wrongful death lawsuit. Seek legal counsel if you've experienced a fetal death during medical training.

Though physician fathers also suffer, medical education creates undue hardship for women of childbearing age who must conceive and carry a child to term (hopefully) and attempt to breastfeed while meeting all the other requirements of training and/or medical practice while working two to three full-time jobs.

The United States Patient Protection and Affordable Care Act requires employers to provide reasonable break time for employees to express breast milk for nursing children for one year after birth each time such employee needs to express the milk.

"My residency didn't support my breastfeeding, although attendings were proponents of breastfeeding. I had to pump on my own time. My breasts felt like they were gonna explode. I couldn't be late for rounds. We were on 80-hour weeks, and pumping would inevitably put you over. The stress strained milk production. Just staying hydrated was hard let alone trying to produce milk to cover daily 30-ounce needs. As a mom, I felt like I let my kids down with lack of production. Friday would come and they'd cluster feed so badly to boost my supply and by Monday the cycle of havoc would restart. My kids definitely noticed a stressful feeding mom versus a relaxed feeding mom."

FMLA (Family Medical Leave Act) is a federal law that requires employers to allow their employees 12 weeks of unpaid maternity (or paternity) leave, yet female physicians are routinely denied their legal rights.

"Like all female residents in my program, I was not supported during my pregnancy. I had my first child during my chief year and the department chair threatened not to let me graduate on time if I took one day more than six weeks with my newborn. Imagine that—an ob/gyn residency refusing to support the rights of their residents to have families. So I prematurely ripped myself from my tiny newborn at exactly six weeks so I could graduate, even though I wanted at least eight weeks, seeing as I had a cesarean. I deal with the 'mommy guilt' of that decision to this day. It's such a shame because I worked like a Hebrew slave for those people (I even worked the day I went into labor, and I finished my rounds completely out of breath, and then had my baby by cesarean-section two hours later). I wasn't alone though. The director actually insinuated to another resident that if she had another child they would fire her. I always thought that was illegal, but unfortunately we don't get any legal protection in residency, and everyone was too afraid to challenge authority (we just wanted to hurry up and graduate). The same guy even sexually harassed another resident, but again, she was too afraid to come forward."

TAKE ACTION NOW

1. Know the laws that protect your rights to procreate, breastfeed, and raise your family. Research official policies regarding procreating and breastfeeding at your medical institution. Make copies for your records.

2. Receive pre and postnatal medical care with a physician outside of your medical organization (and EMR). Document all medical complications you experience as a result of unsafe working conditions that have undermined your ability to conceive, procreate, or breastfeed—in additional to any mental health impacts of unsafe working conditions on you or your family.

3. Track all discrimination, retaliation, and wrongful termination as a result of pregnancy and childbearing. Reference specific chapters on each topic.

4. In cases of maternal or fetal death, contact a personal injury attorney with experience in wrongful death lawsuits as this is a very specialized area of law with state-specific statutes.

5. Document any breach in your human rights to have a family or spend time with your family, including all demeaning comments about pregnancy, fertility, breastfeeding, and physicians with children. Reference <u>Human Rights Violations Documentation Guidelines</u>.

Document Maternal Deprivation

_____

_____

_____

_____

_____

_____

_____

_____

_____

_____

_____

No Mental Health Care

Absence of psychological support for medical professionals with occupationally induced emotional distress who are penalized with loss or restriction of career for seeking help.

Students enter medicine with their mental health on par with or better than their peers, yet physicians are reported to have the highest suicide rate of any profession. Occupationally induced mental health conditions are rampant among doctors. Reference <u>Discrimination, Mental Health Disability</u> to understand the ongoing ADA violations that limit physicians' access to psychological support during their careers.

Anxiety, depression, and suicidal thoughts often begin in medical school. "The stress is incredible—long hours, insane competition, emotional abuse from peers, faculty, school and hospital administrators," explains one student. "Worst of all, you can't talk about it—or you are silenced. You're obliged, if you ever happen to mention you're suicidal, to follow up quickly with, 'I tried your recommendations and now I'm great!' There is no room for discourse."

Physicians not only suffer from chronic human rights violations, they are exposed to extreme tragedy and death with no on-the-job support. Emergency physicians, anesthesiologists, and surgeons are at high risk of developing PTSD. Doctors are often inserted into crime scenes where they are treating both perpetrators and victims. One suicidal surgery intern shared his doubts about saving a man who jumped out of a building when he was caught raping a young girl who was also being treated in an adjacent room. Doctors see babies that have been murdered and abused in manners unimaginable. They see their own colleagues wheeled into the emergency department after suicide attempts—and it's their job to save their dying friends!

What is unconscionable is that doctors are offered no support—and then punished when they ask for help.

Due to the ongoing mental health witch hunt by hospitals, clinics, medical boards, and physician health programs, many physicians drive hundreds of miles out of town, use fake names, and pay cash to get off-the-grid mental health care. One doctor explains, "I've been in practice 20 years and have been on antidepressants and anxiolytics for all of that time. I drive 300 miles to seek care and always pay in cash. I am forced to lie on my state relicensing every year. There is no way in hell I would ever disclose this to the medical board—they are not our friends."

The reason doctors are sneaking out of town for mental health care is because their human rights are being repeatedly violated. Hospitals, medical boards, insurance companies, and employers all think it's their right to know if a doctor has been depressed during a divorce (and read all their private medical records).

When occupationally induced mental health issues are discovered, some doctors are forced into physician health programs at great personal expense where they are mandated to submit to urine drug screens and participate in 12-step programs for drug use—even though they don't use drugs! Doctors have died by suicide under the care of physician health programs.

TAKE ACTION NOW

1. Seek confidential mental health care with your own psychiatrist or therapist who is not part of your medical institution and who guarantees to keep your medical records confidential and out of the hands of your employers, hospitals, and medical boards.

2. Beware of physician health programs. They were primarily founded for doctors with substance abuse problems—usually a late-stage effect of untreated mental health issues in medicine.

3. Start a peer support group within your medical school or specialty. Don't wait until you lose a colleague to suicide.

4. Stop institutional mental health harassment and discrimination of medical professionals. Reference specific chapters for action steps.

5. Document all obstructions to receiving confidential mental health care by your medical institution. Reference <u>Human Rights Violations Documentation Guidelines</u>.

Document No Mental Health Care

_____

_____

_____

_____

_____

_____

_____

_____

_____

_____

_____

_____

_____

_____

_____

_____

_____

_____

_____

_____

Overwork

*Complete mental and/or physical exhaustion in
medical professionals from too much work.*

For overwork leading to death and suicide, reference <u>Karōshi & Karojishi</u>.
This chapter covers non-fatal impacts of overwork in medical professionals.

Medical students and physicians placed in acute or chronic states of
overwork while dealing with life-and-death decision-making often end up
in a state of physiologic crisis that impacts both their physical and mental
health—with long-term health sequelae.

Medical trainees often live in a state of fight-or-flight with their basic
physiologic needs unmet, including extreme deprivation of food, water,
sleep, and elimination necessary for human life. Reference the chapters on
<u>Food Deprivation</u>, <u>Water Deprivation</u>, and <u>Sleep Deprivation</u>.

Intellectually, physicians know that they are working in a first-world
hospital in the United States and that they are not in a war zone; yet, physio-
logically their bodies are in a chronic state of deprivation and fear in a hostile
and inhumane working environment with chronic elevation in cortisol and
epinephrine and increased blood pressure and heart rate, muscle tension,
hypervigilance, and more.

I have spoken to hospitalists who have worked up to 168-hours without
regular access to food, and were found sleeping in a broom closet. On a 72-
hour shift one doctor reported getting only six hours of sleep on the floor of

her hospital. Doctors are the revenue generators for our health systems, yet they are often treated worse than criminals—and blamed as the problem.

Reference <u>Gaslighting</u> for how words like physician "burnout" and "resilience" are used to make physicians feel demeaned, punished, and confused. Amid the blatant human rights violations, "burnout" coaches abound. Perplexed, I asked a top physician "burnout" coach, "Don't you think all your 'burnout' breathing exercises and EMR workarounds just prolong the agony for physicians in toxic working conditions?"

He replied, "Yes."

Since that 2015 conversation, I've been debunking "burnout" as a victim-blaming buzzword that prolongs physician agony by avoiding the real issue leading to physician despair—human rights violations, including overwork that can lead to long-term physical or mental health conditions—even death.

A partial list of the adverse effects of chronic overwork on doctors are: dehydration, hypoglycemia, obesity, constipation, kidney stones, heart attacks, poor eating and exercise, alcohol and drug use, guilt, shame, back and neck pain, hypertension, stroke, seizures, insomnia, panic attacks, PTSD, emotional-detachment, depression, psychosis, and suicide.

All the while, physicians are deprived of a normal personal life with their spouse, children, and family. One surgery program boasted 100 percent divorce rates of trainees. Medical students, residents, and practicing physicians working 100-hour work weeks obviously have neglected spouses, and some experience multiple divorces and strained relationship with children.

<u>TAKE ACTION NOW</u>

1. Limit work hours when possible and take a vacation to reflect on how you truly want to practice medicine. You have choices!

2. You have the right to a safe workplace. If your workplace is unsafe, unhealthful, or hazardous, file an OSHA complaint and request a NIOSH evaluation per instructions in <u>Human Rights Violations Documentation Guidelines</u>.

3. If your job is abusive and prevents you from meeting your physiologic needs for safety and health, quit. Consider opening your own medical practice. Be your own boss. For instructions visit IdealMedicalCare.org.

4. Beware of institutional gaslighting, shaming, and blaming tactics used to make you feel that overworking is normal and that you are the problem.

5. Document unsafe working conditions when forced to work more than 60 hours weekly. Reference <u>Human Rights Violations Documentation Guidelines</u>.

Document Overwork

_____

_____

_____

_____

_____

_____

_____

_____

_____

_____

_____

_____

_____

_____

_____

_____

_____

_____

Pimping

A traditional teaching technique in which a medical trainee is publicly interrogated on medical minutiae until they cry in front of peers, staff, and patients.

Article 26 of the Universal Declaration of Human Rights proclaims: "Education shall be directed to the full development of the human personality and to the strengthening of respect for human rights and fundamental freedoms." Yet medical education is often based upon hierarchy and fear. Pimping is a public interrogation session in which a medical trainee is grilled on obscure medical minutiae. Professors generally pick on the person who is most likely to break down in the group of students. Some pimping sessions are instructional; others are malicious.

Pimping sessions are obviously frightening to some trainees and can leave victims with long-term mental health impacts, even into retirement.

"I'm currently off sick with anxiety/depression—this is my third episode and I'm only 31," reports one physician. "The first episode started in medical school during a particularly unpleasant 'teaching session' where I was ripped apart in front of a patient and my peers. My best friend stood next to me whispering, 'It's okay, it's okay,' in a bid to stop me from breaking down then and there. We moved to the next patient for one of my peers to be cross-examined, when this patient looked at me and offered me a tissue because she could see the tears in my eyes."

The long-term effects may be worse for observers than for the person who is being pimped because of a perceived disempowerment in witnesses. Observers are mute, invisible—and feel powerless to help someone they see suffering. When others in the group remain silent, the attending creates an illusion of group support and unity for his tactics since nobody generally risks standing up for the student being pimped. If students don't protest public humiliation sessions, pimping becomes the norm during the rotation.

Those that perform best during pimping sessions are trainees who are able to retain some sense of boundaries and not feel personally persecuted. Men are more intolerant to public humiliation than women and will speak up sooner. When they get the answer wrong they can be challenged, and are less likely to tolerate humiliation. Having a clear sense of self and a strong knowledge base is protective. Individuals are less likely to feel personally attacked when they recognize, "It's not me, it's my knowledge base." When trainees retain boundaries and self-protect in front of witnesses, the entire group is empowered.

TAKE ACTION NOW

1. Stop pimping sessions by disengaging with these simple interventions:

   Student: "You've brought something to my attention that I don't know. I'll research that and come back with an answer."

   Witness: "I don't think any of us know the answer. Let's look it up together."

   Teacher: "Wait a minute. I think there's a more effective way for me to try to help you learn this information."

2. Refuse to be victimized and protect your peers. Remember one person can transform the whole dynamic just by taking their personal power back and not allowing oneself to be a victim.

3. Document all episodes of malicious (and non-malicious) pimping. Note whether these pimping episodes enhanced or distracted from your learning.

Document Pimping

Punishment when Sick

Penalizing a medical student or physician for developing a medical illness.

Beyond discrimination and harassment for chronic health conditions, physicians and medical students are often forced to work—and be in class taking tests—when acutely ill, even during life-threatening emergencies, as these individuals report:

"I was very sick with a stomach bug and vomiting between every patient I saw in clinic. I got so dehydrated I passed out in the hallway during clinic and my nurse called EMS. I had been told that not coming to work that day would result in getting fired. I ended up admitted to the hospital with acute renal failure. My boss reprimanded me for inconveniencing patients."

Hospitals frequently place the lives of hospitalized patients at risk when doctors with contagious diseases are forced to keep working. These physicians share how they were threatened, harassed, and mandated to work while severely ill.

"I'm a family medicine doc and during one of my ob/gyn rotations I came down with pneumonia. The ob attending refused to let me leave. I was running a fever of 104 so they just gave me Tylenol and put an IV in my left hand to keep me hydrated between deliveries. I would just double glove to protect myself. As the night wore on I became worse and my own family medicine attending saw me and proceeded to give me Phenergan IV and told the ob attending that I couldn't work anymore. She called my wife to pick me up and take me home. If not for that one act of kindness, I would have had to stay and deliver babies while sick and then go to gynecology clinic the next morning working a 30-hour shift. The next day, I saw my doc who prescribed antibiotics. My ob attending was so furious that he gave me extra work to do the rest of my rotation."

"My attending told me he worked until his appendix burst and he collapsed. This was given as an example of a good work ethic. In residency I had Guillain-Barré. Not horrible, I never had to be on a ventilator. But I could not use my hands as they were nearly paralyzed. Walking I would have to lean to get momentum and even then it was difficult. Chief resident joked that he gets to intubate. They were trying to figure out how I could take call if I was any worse. I took no time off during that illness, again viewed as weak if you did."

"I had a meningitis (proved by spinal tap and hospitalized for three days during my second year of residency). Subsequently developed some depression, worsened by the fact that I initially complained about my residency program requiring me to 'pay back' the three days of work I missed while hospitalized (to work three extra shifts on my days off). I complained because I was contractually entitled to sick leave. These were the only three days of work I missed over a total of five years of residency. In return for complaining, I was told a couple of months later that someone had noticed my attitude had changed (it had) and my knowledge base was deficient (it was not). I was asked to submit to a random urine drug test (which of course I passed). I told my residency director that yes, my attitude had changed—I was depressed about how the program was treating me—and that I agreed I would benefit from some counseling (which I arranged for privately, without further interference from my program). The following month, I tested in the 98th percentile nationwide on my residency in-service exam (higher, in fact, than any other resident in my program). It turns out that my perceived 'knowledge gap' was real: I knew more about emergency medicine than some of my upperclassmen. When test results returned, their criticism stopped."

Tasked with training the next generation of doctors, teaching hospitals and medical schools should set the gold standard for health care. Instead our hospitals and medical schools are routinely violating the human rights of our medical students and doctors who become ill—even when their health conditions are occupationally induced and contagious.

Physical health discrimination and harassment in medicine is a clear human rights violation illegal in the United States under the Americans with Disabilities Act.

TAKE ACTION NOW

1. Review the Discrimination, Harassment, and Retaliation chapters for additional action steps.

2. Make copies of your medical institution's policy on sick leave and understand your rights under FMLA (Family Medical Leave Act).

3. You have the right to a safe workplace. If your workplace is unsafe, unhealthful, or hazardous, file an OSHA complaint and request a NIOSH evaluation per instructions in Human Rights Violations Documentation Guidelines.

4. Document everything and make sure your personal physician does the same. Reference Human Rights Violations Documentation Guidelines.

Document Punishment when Sick

_____

_____

_____

_____

_____

_____

_____

_____

_____

_____

Question Quashing

Mistreating medical students or physicians for asking questions resulting in question phobia among victims and witnesses.

Higher education should be a time of enlightenment in which questions are welcomed and curiosity is encouraged. Asking questions is integral to learning and is a human right protected by the First Amendment of the United States Constitution that guarantees freedom of speech. Article 19 of the Universal Declaration of Human Rights confirms: "everyone has the right to freedom of opinion and expression; this right includes freedom to hold opinions without interference and to seek, receive and impart information and ideas through any media and regardless of frontiers."

Despite these protections, some medical trainees are labeled as too curious or outspoken and feel thwarted in their education as these female physicians report:

"I was very outspoken before medical school and that had to stop, because I would be invalidated at every turn and told I had psychiatric issues."

"I was labeled as unprofessional for raising my hand in a class to help a classmate with a question. The professor couldn't answer the question and his back was to me so I had to say the professor's name and ask permission if I could answer my classmate. For that I was later emailed by the professor and told I was unprofessional and rude. I was in no way either unprofessional or rude. I truly believe that the male professor was upset because he didn't know the answer. His email lashing me for trying to help another student was unbelievable."

These tactics have a negative impact on medical education and may create an environment of distrust and fear adversely impacting relationships with future physicians. Doctors who have been silenced are less likely to trust each other. Reference Bullying, Intimidation, and Pimping.

"It would be many years before I recovered from the fear of the motive behind a question," reports an obstetrician. "The sad thing is I now realize most people are not coming at you in attack mode, and I had missed out on a lot of opportunities. Most of my colleagues, it seems to me, have never recovered. Physicians do not befriend one another. They are either arrogant and don't need friends, or distrusting and will never let you in."

Ultimately the fear of asking a question and risk of being publicly humiliated not only undermines medical education, and collegial trust, it prevents physicians and trainees from honestly expressing themselves when discussing patients.

"Medicine often endorses a culture of groupthink that discourages dissent, discussion, and individuality," an internist reports. "The further I progressed in my training, despite acquisition of more skills and knowledge, the more fearful I became. Criticism in various forms never ended. The further my confidence dwindled and I became more outwardly hesitant (despite feeling inwardly confident about my answer or plan) the more colleagues questioned my decisions. This may have to do with my almost extreme introversion and difficulty asserting myself. I watched colleagues often act and speak very confidently even when I knew they didn't totally know what they were talking about. I never mastered this skill of acting confident even when in doubt. I felt it was disingenuous. My true opinions on what was best for a patient were frequently different from the group. I became afraid of expressing myself, even when I knew I was absolutely correct. Before medical school I was never afraid to be a dissenting voice, but I learned in residency that it did not matter if I was correct—disagreeing with someone higher up than myself, even if in the interest of patient safety, was not in my best interest."

Physician trainees who are silenced and unable to ask or answer questions without fear may experience lifelong adverse impacts on their ability to communicate. A very close physician friend revealed to me that decades after completing residency she is still extremely nervous before asking a question of any physician who she believes may be more knowledgeable—including me!

TAKE ACTION NOW

1. Remember you have a human right to freedom of speech. You have a right to ask questions. Exercise your rights.

2. Unite with your colleagues. Encourage free flow of conversation to build trust and for the benefit of patient care.

3. Keep a list of your questions below and consult with a trusted mentor for answers if you feel unsafe asking your attending. Document situations when you feel unsafe to ask a question.

Document Question Quashing

_____

_____

_____

_____

_____

_____

_____

_____

_____

_____

_____

_____

_____

_____

Retaliation

An adverse action taken against a medical student or physician who exercises a protected legal right.

Retaliation is illegal when the action preceding the retaliation is protected by law. Physician trainees often experience retaliation when complaining about harassment and discrimination. Reference <u>Discrimination</u>, <u>Harassment</u>, and <u>Retaliation</u>.

"When I spoke up about an attending groping me at the scrub sink, the physician in charge of my residency program told me, 'He brings money into this hospital and you don't. Either shut up or get out of the program.' After that, I was seen as the problem."

One obstetrician known for his threats and abuse of residents would end checkout with, "Your daddy's lawyer can't save you from me!"

"I was a new physician in my dream job, five months pregnant, when my 15-month-old had a febrile seizure in the middle of the night. I called out. I was nervous. I returned to my shift once my husband came home. The next day a nasty email arrived in my inbox accusing me of lacking accountability, integrity, and 'burnout.' 'My baby had a seizure,' I said to myself in disbelief. I took my concerns to the director of this major health corporation only to be written up for 'lack of integrity' and 'burnout.' The mistreatment did not stop. I was left in two 12-hour shifts in a row, not allowed to leave at six months pregnant. As a gestational diabetic with a high-volume patient load and no proper staffing. I would lie on the bathroom floor in between patients because I was in and out of consciousness as I could not eat properly for fear I would be written up if a patient complained they were not seen fast enough. When my supervisor would 'drop by,' he commented, 'We need to hire more men; they don't get pregnant.' Women at this company keep coming forward with similar tales so I sought help from federal agencies tasked with protecting us from discrimination and workplace bullying only to be told if I had not been sexually assaulted and/or fired wrongfully, I had limited rights."

"I failed my first emergency medicine rotation in third year because I had a miscarriage. I had to take two weeks off and the attending agreed to pass me for a two-week rotation, but then didn't. All I ever wanted to be was an emergency doc. The subsequent glowing recommendations I received from other emergency rotations didn't help. All residencies saw was that failure. And my school let it stand. Apparently, you're supposed to still be on rotation and seeing patients with your baby falling out of your uterus."

Retaliation even impacts the lives of physicians protecting their peers.

"Where I went to residency, the male faculty (married) were having sex with female residents in the call rooms. One female resident attempted suicide due to the pressure. I blew the whistle to the dean over our program. I was thrown out of residency. Years later, they still give me a hard time, and have allowed tampered education records to remain in my file because it was 'my fault' for blowing the whistle."

TAKE ACTION NOW

1. Reference <u>Discrimination</u> and <u>Harassment</u> for specific action steps in your situation.

2. Educate and protect other medical professionals who are experiencing retaliation when speaking up about human rights violations in medicine.

3. Avoid submitting complaints internally without legal counsel. Remember Human Resources protects your employer, not you. Your case is solid if you have documentation and an attorney representing you.

4. Document, document, document! Reference <u>Human Rights Violations</u>
   <u>Documentation Guidelines</u>.

Document Retaliation

_____

_____

_____

_____

_____

_____

_____

_____

_____

_____

_____

_____

_____

_____

_____

_____

_____

_____

_____

_____

_____

_____

_____

Sleep Deprivation

Extreme lack of sleep that may lead to the injury or death of medical professionals and their patients.

"No one shall be subjected to torture or to cruel, inhuman or degrading treatment or punishment" and "Everyone has the right to rest and leisure, including reasonable limitation of working hours and periodic holidays with pay," according to the Universal Declaration of Human Rights. Sleep deprivation is recognized internationally as a torture technique and a violation of human rights. Yet in medicine, sleep deprivation is a lifestyle, a rite of passage—even a badge of honor. Of all human rights violations inflicted upon medical students and physicians, sleep deprivation is most destabilizing and acutely life-threatening—as this doctor recounts:

"I did my internship in internal medicine and residency in neurology before laws existed to regulate resident hours. My first two years were extremely brutal, working 120 hours per week and up to 40 hours straight. I witnessed colleagues collapse unconscious in the hallway during rounds, and I recall once falling asleep in the bed of an elderly comatose woman while trying to start an IV on her in the wee hours of the morning."

Residents traditionally worked unlimited hours until 1984 when college student Libby Zion died in a New York hospital. Her father, Sidney Zion, a well-connected lawyer and journalist, stated, "I left her there with an earache and a fever and they sent her home in a box." He soon discovered that her care was left to sleep-deprived residents without supervision. Legal battles culminated in a 1989 New York Health Department requirement that doctors-in-training have adequate supervision and work no more than 24 consecutive hours with an average work week of 80 hours. In 2003 the ACGME (Accreditation Council for Graduate Medical Education) applied these work-hour limits to all United States residents and in 2011 capped first-year residents' shifts at 16 hours.

Despite all the new laws, duty-hour restrictions remain unenforced so residents may still work unlimited hours, as this doctor reveals, "In general surgery residency, I had one week in which I worked 125 hours. I did a weekend of 72 hours in which I only got four hours of sleep. I would secretly hope to get in a car accident and maybe break a leg so that I would be forced to take off from work just so I could get some rest."

Sleep-deprived residents are at high risk of harming themselves and others. Many develop suicidal daydreams. Some actually die by suicide as a direct result of sleep deprivation.

In 2016, a physician friend and I gathered more than 75,000 signatures on a petition delivered personally to Dr. Thomas Nasca, CEO of ACGME, demanding the agency take action to address sleep deprivation and rampant human rights violations in medical training that lead to so many suicides among our medical students and doctors.

I received a letter thanking me for the petition and declaring that the ACGME is committed to creating "safe learning environments that serve the best interests of our residents and fellows and the patients in their care." Despite our petition and a public opinion poll revealing that 86 percent of Americans oppose lifting the 16-hour cap on first-year doctors, the ACGME made the reckless decision to increase shifts on new doctors from 16 to 28 hours and would permit residents to work *unlimited* hours without having to justify why.

Despite overwhelming scientific evidence on the dangers of sleep deprivation, the ACGME claims sleep-deprived doctors working longer hours could make patient care safer due to improved continuity of care with the same doctor. Yet medical errors are one of the many catastrophic consequences of forcing doctors to work beyond their physiologic capacity without adequate sleep.

Residents don't complain when programs violate work-hour restrictions due to retaliation from program directors who may label them as inefficient or undermine their entire career. Reference <u>Forced Drugging</u> and <u>Lying</u> for more details. Complaints could lead to an ACGME investigation and loss of accreditation for the entire residency, adversely impacting the future of all physicians in the program. So nobody says anything. Violations continue. Patients die. Physicians suffer. Doctors die in post-call car accidents because they're unsafe to drive home after work.

Sleep deprivation is more dangerous than driving under the influence of alcohol. In fact, being awake for at least 24 hours is like having a blood alcohol concentration of 0.08 percent (beyond the legal limit in the United States). Here are harrowing tales of physicians just trying to get home after a shift. Sadly, some never make it.

"I ran a red light driving home in residency after a 36-hour shift. Got pulled over. It was sobering: I was not fit to use my driver's license, but I had just been using my medical license for over a day nonstop!"

"During internship I was driving home after a 30-hour call. I got on the highway going the wrong direction. Thankfully, a police car pulled me over as I was going into oncoming traffic. He escorted me all the way home."

"A dear friend from med school died during her neurosurgery residency. Drove over a median into a tractor trailer after a 30-plus hour shift. She left behind her family, including a twin sister and her fiancé. She was thirty."

<u>TAKE ACTION NOW</u>

1. Always ask your doctors how long they've been on shift. You have the right to request a doctor who is alert and well-rested. Your doctor has a human right to sleep.

2. File a confidential complaint with OSHA, the Joint Commission, and ACGME to have your workplace inspected when sleep deprivation is a hazard to human health. Seek legal counsel for further help. Reference <u>Human Rights Violations Documentation Guidelines</u>.

3. File a complaint with the New York State Department of Health under the 405 Regulations if you have sustained work-hour violations in New York, where medical trainees sustain greater assaults yet have greater

protections than physicians in the rest of the United States. (This was made possible thanks to Libby dad, Sidney Zion.) ACGME policies may in conflict with your state laws. If you feel your rights have been breached in New York, contact IdealMedicalCare.org for specific legal help.

4. Document all episodes of sleep deprivation that have endangered the lives of medical professionals or their patients.

Document Sleep Deprivation

Suicide

Wrongful death of a medical trainee or physician subjected to human rights violations in medicine.

We have a right to life, liberty, happiness—*and safe working conditions.* Wrongful death claims can be filed against a medical institution that has caused the death of a medical student or physician by negligence or through intentional harm. Unlike other human rights violations in medicine that require legal action by the victim, wrongful death claims allow the estate of the suicided doctor to sue the party legally liable for the death. Surviving family members are the plaintiffs and must prove the case on behalf of the deceased medical student or physician. Immediate legal counsel is crucial in the aftermath of a medical student or physician suicide.

All deaths of overworked medical professionals are handled by workers' compensation in Japan. Reference Karōshi & Karojishi (physician death and physician suicide by overwork) that describes how victims' families apply for workers' compensation benefits when their loved ones die as a result of overwork. So there is international precedent—companies *are held liable* for suicides due to harmful working conditions.

Since 2012, I've been running a suicide helpline for medical students and physicians. Most are severely overworked and have suffered multiple human rights violations by the time they reach out for help.

To date, I've spoken to thousands of suicidal doctors; published a book of their suicide letters; led their memorials and candlelight vigils; and met with countless surviving friends and families. I've spent nearly every waking moment over the past seven years on a personal quest for the truth of why doctors are dying by suicide.

At the time of publication, I have compiled and investigated nearly 1,300 medical student and doctor suicides—and these cases are the tip of the iceberg. I never went looking for doctor suicides. Most cases were submitted by loved ones and colleagues reaching out to me for help. As a result, I've interviewed surviving family members, physician friends, and staff to inform my data and research into this hidden epidemic.

The fact is nearly all suicide victims would be alive today had they been pilots or pet groomers. Instead they were placed directly in harm's way and sustained chronic human rights violations without protection by the laws that safeguard the lives of all other workers.

Doctors choose suicide to end their pain—not because they want to die. Ignoring doctor suicides just leads to more doctor suicides. We can actually help doctors who are suffering now and prevent their suicides. To save lives, we must stop the secrecy and face reality. Our doctors are being abused. Some victims view suicide as their only way out.

Physician suicides should be reported to OSHA as workplace fatalities. Reference <u>Karōshi & Karojishi.</u>

Legal action is required to end the human rights violations that lead to physician suicides. Of these 1,300 suicides, only a few families have launched wrongful death lawsuits. Even if unsuccessful, a wrongful death lawsuit will publicly document human rights violations sustained by doctors at their own medical institutions for the entire world to view.

TAKE ACTION NOW

1. Please be aware the statute of limitations is two years on wrongful death lawsuits. A surviving spouse must file a wrongful death lawsuit on behalf of their deceased spouse. Parents must file the wrongful death lawsuit on behalf of an unmarried medical student or physician. Wrongful death claims seek compensation for medical and funeral expenses, loss of future earnings, financial support (including educational assistance), and loss of care, comfort, and companionship.

2. Immediately request records of your hospitalizations and medical evaluations. If you are obstructed in any way from receiving medical records within 30 days of your request, you may need legal counsel for help with medical institutions withholding or altering evidence.

3. Contact an attorney with experience in wrongful death lawsuits as this is a very specialized area of law with state-specific statutes, and cases are challenging to prove.

4. Request the annual log of work-related injury and deaths at your institution to assure suicides are reported properly to OSHA.

5. Document all medical student and physician suicides below by name, age, specialty, date of death, and method of suicide. Please submit suicides confidentially through IdealMedicalCare.org so victims can be added to the suicide registry and surviving families may receive free confidential support.

Document Medical Student & Physician Suicides

_____

_____

_____

_____

_____

_____

_____

_____

_____

_____

_____

_____

_____

Termination, Wrongful

Illegal termination (or illegal dismissal from medical school) in violation of a medical student's or physician's rights or contract.

If you are wrongfully terminated from your job or wrongfully dismissed from medical training, you may have grounds to challenge the action. This area of law is complex and you will need an attorney to guide you. The primary categories under which your wrongful termination may be filed are the following:

Contract breach means that you were fired in violation of your employment agreement. Refer to your written contract to establish whether your termination followed permissible contractual reasons. Your employer may also have an employee handbook that covers termination and disciplinary actions. If you have documented emails or verbal promises of guaranteed employment or tenure, that documentation should be given to your legal counsel to determine if you have grounds for wrongful termination.

Discrimination is mistreatment by a medical institution or employer of a medical professional based upon a status protected by anti-discrimination law. It is against the law to be terminated based on age, mental or physical disability, race, gender, or other protected status. Reference <u>Discrimination</u> for action steps and seek legal counsel.

Harassment is unwelcome or offensive conduct, based upon a protected legal status, that creates a hostile work environment for a medical professional. The law protects you from being fired based upon age, gender, race, mental or physical disability, or other protected category. Reference <u>Harassment</u> for action steps and seek legal counsel.

Retaliation is an illegal action when taken against a protected legal right. You have a wrongful termination case if you experienced retaliation for filing a complaint with an outside agency for discrimination, harassment, safety violations, medical leave violations, or other human rights violations in medicine. Reference <u>Retaliation</u> for specific details and actions.

Fraud is illegal and when perpetrated by an employer during recruitment or hiring/firing (such as when a physician is induced to resign), and it is grounds for a wrongful termination case. You must document the fraud and demonstrate that it was intentional and used in an effort to deceive you. Seek legal counsel for assistance.

Defamation is grounds for a wrongful termination lawsuit if your employer or medical institution made malicious or false statements about you that prevented you from acquiring new employment. Gather comprehensive documentation and seek legal counsel.

Whistleblowing is protected by law. If you reported illegal activity at your medical institution that harms the public interest, or filed grievances with enforcement agencies related to whistleblowing and were terminated as a result, then you may have a wrongful termination case. Seek legal counsel.

<u>TAKE ACTION NOW</u>

1. Medical students, residents, and physicians require specific legal counsel dependent on category of wrongful termination/dismissal and the medical institution involved.

2. Unite with other victims who have been wrongfully terminated from your medical institution.

3. Documentation is key to prevailing in wrongful termination cases. Reference <u>Human Rights Violations Documentation Guidelines</u> and track details below.

Document Wrongful Termination

_____

_____

_____

_____

_____

_____

_____

_____

_____

_____

_____

_____

_____

_____

_____

_____

_____

_____

_____

_____

_____

_____

_____

_____

Threat

A declaration of intent to inflict punishment upon a medical student or physician in retribution for an (in)action.

We all have a right to a safe educational and work environment. Yet medical students and physicians may be subject to threats by superiors who wish to control their behavior. Most commonly, medical professionals receive threats of harm to their career or educational trajectory in retribution for an (in) action, or failure to comply with a future action. Examples of threats:

A physician became teary at work on the anniversary of her suicide attempt. She told her boss she needed a minute. Instead of giving her a few minutes to recover, her boss told the doctor to go home and threatened to fire her.

Attending physician says, "If you displease me, you will never work again in surgery."

On the day preceding his suicide as a whistleblower, orthopedic surgeon Dr. Ortiz received a phone call in the doctors' lounge. Staff said he was white as a ghost and they believe he must have been threatened.

When a female physician requests to be paid an amount equal to a male physician for computer training, her manager says he wonders if she is the "right fit" for the job, in essence, threatening her with termination.

After a trainee made a minor spelling error on a patient chart, the emergency department physician brought her to a quiet spot and told her that this mistake meant she was completely incompetent and he would contact the faculty to dismiss her.

A medicine attending selects attractive female students for rotation and tells them if they don't "put out" they won't get a good evaluation.

A resident complains about attending groping her at the scrub sink and the program director tells her to "shut up or get out of the program."

An attending says, "If the family sues, you're going down with me."

To a foreign doctor, "If you don't like it here, go back to your country."

Patient wanting refill threatens to be back with a gun. Employer sides with patient. True story. Another physician friend shared: "A patient threatened to kill me and I was reprimanded. My employer backed the patient!"

TAKE ACTION NOW

1. Always take action in response to a threat.

2. Unite with colleagues who may be victims of similar threats. Track threats against your peers and teach them to document and stand up for themselves.

3. Document every single threat. Sometimes an isolated threat can lead to a wrongful termination or a discrimination lawsuit. Without documenting the most minor threat, you may not be able to prove a future case. Reference Human Rights Violations Documentation Guidelines.

Document Threats

_____

_____

_____

_____

_____

_____

_____

Unethical Activity

*Immoral, dishonest, or deceitful activities forced upon a medical
student or physician as part of their education or employment.*

Despite attempts to bolster humanism in medical education, most students
and residents experience declining empathy and increasing cynicism during
training. Much of their disillusionment and despair is the result of being
asked to participate in activities they consider unethical. Activities that are
unethical may also be illegal.

Article 26 of the Universal Declaration of Human Rights proclaims:
"Education shall be directed to the full development of the human personality and to the strengthening of respect for human rights and fundamental
freedoms."

Yet within the hidden curriculum of medical training, students often encounter unethical and illegal behavior. Question medical students on day one
of medical school, "If asked to do something inappropriate by an attending,
would you do it?" Most students say yes. By graduation even more students
would submit to inappropriate and unethical acts.

During my medical training we were mandated to kill dogs in animal
labs as first-year medical students. In the "Events of the Cardiac Cycle" lab,
four students are assigned to each dog. Instructions: Inject the live dog with
epinephrine and study the EKG. Sever cardiac nerves. Carve open the chest
and shock the heart. As the dog's blood pressure drops, remove the heart.

Now, stab the aorta with a scissor and slice open the ventricle. Check for heartworms. Bag the carcass, and clean your instruments and work station.

In a petition, I stated my personal intention not to kill and circulated the petition to classmates. From among the 189 students, three shared my moral objections and signed on. I circulated a second petition for others to support our right to opt out of animal labs, but no classmates signed due to "fear of being blacklisted from residencies."

Then I sent a letter to the physiology director stating that I would not participate in animal experiments.

"These are not animal experiments," he replied. "They are *experiences*. Attendance is mandatory. You are assigned to Team 11B. An unexcused absence will compromise your teammates' education and prevent your matriculation into the clinical core."

Ultimately I met with the dean who diagnosed me with *Bambi Syndrome.* He belittled me for having compassion for animals, though did grant my exemption from the lab. My classmates all participated in the brutal experience.

Unethical experiences in medical training are too numerous to list. At some point during their training, most students feel pressured to act unethically. Trainees have been asked to perform pelvic examinations on women under general anesthesia without patient consent. During my gynecology rotation, they wheeled in demented ladies from the nursing home for routine Pap smears. New doctors overhear derogatory remarks about patients and are then left unsupervised caring for the critically ill. One student recently shared that she was forced to memorize and use a surgeon's login and password to three different EMR systems which she told him she was not comfortable doing.

Standing up for your ethics and defending your patients can be an isolating experience in medicine. Don't back down.

"Three times this month, I told my boss I would not commit insurance fraud," shares a doctor. "The first time I was called unprofessional. Then I was labeled, not a team player. And finally I was written up as disruptive."

Poor patient care begins with institutionalized unethical behavior that inevitably leads to medical mistakes and patient harm.

One person can make a difference. The dog labs I once protested have now been removed from all medical schools. Your voice matters.

TAKE ACTION NOW

1. Unite with peers to change the culture at your medical institution. Start a petition. Refuse to accept unethical activities as a normal part of medical culture. Reach out to a trusted mentor. If you need help, contact me at IdealMedicalCare.org.

2. Inaction when faced with unethical activity makes you an accomplice in these events and risks your involvement in more serious unethical activities during your career. Always be true to your values, and medicine will be a fabulous and fulfilling profession.

3. Document all unethical activities in your curriculum or at your medical institution below. Speak up. Seek professional counsel early.

Document Unethical Activity

_____

_____

_____

_____

_____

_____

_____

_____

_____

_____

_____

_____

_____

_____

_____

_____

Violence

*The intentional use of physical force to injure
a medical student or physician.*

The Universal Declaration of Human Rights Article 3 states: "Everyone has the right to life, liberty and security of person." We all have the right to live in freedom and safety, yet inside our hospitals our own medical students and physicians are sometimes physically and sexually assaulting each other—and being killed.

"As a petite female resident wearing scrubs with white coat, I was standing writing an inpatient note at a corner of a nurses' station when I suddenly found a huge thigh between my legs, spreading my legs wider, pinning me against the desk so I could not move. I froze in shock. After about ten seconds, what felt like forever, the foreign thigh finally let up. I turned around to see my fellow resident, smirking at me and walking away. I finished rounds and went to the male attending. He told me I was 'too sensitive, it was likely nothing.' I went to the female family medicine attending and was told, 'It was just a good gesture, just having fun.'"

In the operating room, bullying can escalate from screaming and name calling to throwing scalpels at students: "I started medical school in Germany. It's very abusive from the get go. Your superiors could do anything with you: I mean hit you, I mean throw knives at you, and it was completely okay because you were happy you had a position as a doctor. Then I got a scholarship to move to France. They had more of a physician shortage, but it was still so highly abusive in medical school. There was one surgical department where every single day all the professors said mean things, yelling at students and residents in the OR. Eventually I was invited to study in the States and I moved to California. I remember one ER doc, he always hit me on the shoulder if I gave the wrong answer."

Another student reports, "An orthopedic surgeon put me in the corner and yelled at me for nearly an hour to make me cry after he threw a scalpel at the other student in the operating room."

Patients also may physically assault physicians and in rare cases enter a medical facility with a gun and kill physicians. Three friends recently shared threats of gun violence from their patients wanting refills and threatening to return with a gun. Unbelievably, the employers sided with patients and reprimanded all three physicians.

Killing physicians inside hospitals is more common overseas. Since guns are less available in other countries, doctors are assaulted with large kitchen knives. My dear friend from China has witnessed colleagues stabbed to death by patients and their families inside her training hospital. Cases are censored and murderers are not punished. Afraid to wear her white coat due to the potential for violence, she left China in fear for her life as a physician.

TAKE ACTION NOW

1. If your medical institution fails to safeguard you from violence or to offer a secure work environment, report your concern to the authorities, including the local police department.

2. File a restraining order if you are at risk of significant danger.

3. Heed your intuition—your gut sense that forewarns you of danger. Better to respond quickly than to hesitate. Doctors have been killed and risk fatal consequences from inaction.

4. Document all violence and threats of violence to your medical institution and take protective action to prevent physical harm to yourself or others.

Document Violence

Water Deprivation

*Lack of access to hydration essential for normal function
of the human body of a medical professional.*

Medical professionals are well aware of the impact of water deprivation on the human body. When our physiologic needs for hydration are unmet, the body struggles to function. Dehydration can lead to loss of energy, fatigue, thirst, headaches, constipation, kidney stones, increased heart rate, dizziness, fainting, and other adverse effects that will not bode well for patient care.

"A friend of mine, an ED doc, works at a site where they have just been told they can't even have water at their desks. Mind you, they run all day, barely have time to eat and have to document and order nonstop on the EMR. But a glass of water? Nope. Cruel."

"The most important thing I learned about self-care was from my inpatient medicine senior. He showed us where the water/ice machine was in the ED and told us multiple times that the most important thing, no matter what emergency was in the ED, was to keep ourselves hydrated. Many of the other specialties expected you to eat and drink in a hurry, if we ate at all."

"One resident went into diabetic ketoacidosis and required hospitalization for several days because of our irregular access to food and water."

In prolonged surgeries, physicians will limit liquids before the procedure so they won't need to disrupt the surgery to urinate. Surgeons may end up dehydrated, dizzy, or fainting in the operating room and then get berated by chief wellness officers for not hydrating!

Of course, the well-hydrated physician ends up with a full bladder and some trainees fear going to the bathroom because they'll be told that they're not team players. Surgeons wear adult diapers to avoid bathroom breaks during procedures. My friend survived surgical training thanks to a steady supply of diapers, chocolate bars, and coffee. Self-employed doctors continue to hold their bladders until they realize that in their own clinics they can urinate whenever they want! After years of water deprivation, some doctors continue to have lifelong abnormal bowel and bladder function.

TAKE ACTION NOW

1. Request a copy of the workplace labor laws governing your right to breaks and meals. If there are no guidelines for physicians, unite with your colleagues and petition for a safe working environment that prevents medical professionals from fainting from dehydration or developing other life-threatening conditions that may impair our ability to safely care for patients.

2. Defend your right to drink when you are thirsty and urinate when your bladder is full. Know where the closest bathrooms are and utilize them at minimum every four hours. If you are not urinating, or your urine is dark, you are dehydrated.

3. Carry plenty of hydrating snacks and drinks for yourself and your colleagues who may be dehydrated. Always carry a water bottle.

4. Document all episodes of water deprivation that endanger the lives of medical professionals or their patients. Reference <u>Human Rights Violations Documentation Guidelines</u>.

Document Water Deprivation

_____

_____

_____

Xenophobia

*Prejudice against medical students or physicians
from other cultures.*

Western medicine has historically been a good-old-boys' club. As we transition from a paternalistic reductionist medical model to a more complementary holistic and global paradigm, some will not welcome the change. More discrimination and harassment of foreign medical professionals may result. Much of the bias originates with patients and staff.

Foreign doctors have their visas sponsored by smaller hospitals and health centers in underserved areas and they may find patients in rural America don't want to see them.

"As an Indian-American medical student (who is a United States citizen), I've had multiple patients say 'no foreign doctors.'"

"I experience racism all the time from patients. Sometimes it's well-intentioned, like when old ladies tell me I look like a 'little china doll' but other times it's because they would prefer a white doctor. I've had attendings bluntly ask what my ethnicity is. Which is annoying and a bit jarring."

"My patient yelled at staff that he would not see his assigned PCP from the HMO because he had yellow skin."

"My residency was in a big Midwest town where little old ladies taking the same elevator at my apartment complex with me would turn and say, 'When are you going home?' or simply, 'Go home.'"

TAKE ACTION NOW

1. Reference <u>Discrimination</u> and <u>Harassment</u> and follow action steps.

2. Immigrants are protected under United States anti-discrimination laws. Refer to Equal Employment Opportunity Commission for legal support. Know your rights and document every instance when they are violated.

3. Join together with other immigrants at your medical institution and create one set of documentation to present to your superiors. Identify colleagues who witness the abuse and are willing to attest to that. Ask for their help by providing depositions stating what they have seen.

4. If your superiors fail to take action, present your documentation to the Immigrant and Employee Rights Section in the Department of Justice's Civil Rights Division and seek legal counsel.

5. Document all instances of discrimination and harassment of foreign doctors and medical trainees below and prepare responses in advance in case you find yourself in a similar situation again.

Document Xenophobia

_____

_____

_____

_____

_____

_____

_____

_____

_____

_____

Yelling

Shouting at a medical student or doctor.

Though yelling during an emergency in an effort to save a patient's life may be acceptable, use of verbal violence against a medical professional is a form of intimidation that should not be tolerated by medical institutions. Yelling is counterproductive as a teaching tool and often will not only fail to motivate a trainee to learn, a verbal assault may also cause the student to isolate, cower, and disengage from their medical education. Yelling may even lead to long-term mental health sequelae in witnesses and patients.

Article 26 of the Universal Declaration of Human Rights proclaims: "Education shall be directed to the full development of the human personality and to the strengthening of respect for human rights and fundamental freedoms."

Verbal violence may be perpetuated by a superior, a peer, or even a patient or their family member. Without intervention by those who witness verbal assaults in our health care facilities, violence will continue to be accepted as the norm and may escalate to physical violence. Yelling degrades the learning environment for everyone, leading to hostile working conditions that are illegal.

Here are examples of yelling that should never be tolerated in medicine:

"I was a first-year resident scrubbed in on a case with a 'difficult' attending known to yell and scream during surgery. During the case, he screamed,

'Retract, bitch!' and I retracted the patient's flesh so hard, I broke off a piece of the patient's chest wall!"

During an operating room pimping session, a medical student responded properly to a question asking her to list the vessels supplying an organ. The surgeon accused the student of lying. The student defended her response as being in the textbook. Her preceptor jumped in and started yelling that the student was calling the surgeon a liar and kicked her out of the operating theater and the rotation.

Once yelling is accepted within medical institutions, the behavior can escalate and involve patient attacks on physicians as this doctor shares: "I have patients yelling at me when all I want to do is help. They try to fool me and manipulate me. Insurance companies deny my patients help—leaving me with no resources to help. My boss is a douche—unethical and danger-ous. I want to build relationships and do what's right for my patients, but the company pushes me to see more and more patients in less and less time. I cry at work, I cry myself to sleep sometimes."

A special note on yelling by family members in the aftermath of a loved one's death: Trauma surgeons and emergency physicians are often placed in the unenviable situation of having to tell a family that their child has died. Trauma surgeons have told me that they bring hospital security guards with them during these conversations due to the potential for violence. Families will shout, scream, and sometimes physically assault the physician if they perceive that the doctor was responsible for their child's death. Grief-stricken individuals may become irrational in their response to unbearable tragedy, yet physical and verbal assaults on physicians must never be tolerated in our health care facilities.

In other countries (much less common in the United States) families have even murdered doctors they believe were responsible for a family member's death. All medical institutions must have policies and procedures in place to safeguard the lives of their medical professionals.

TAKE ACTION NOW

1. Refuse to be victimized or enable the abuse of a victim. Step forward as a witness and intervene. Never allow verbal violence to be accepted as a teaching strategy.

2. Unite with other victims or witnesses to petition your department or medical institution for action. Reference <u>Discrimination</u> and <u>Harassment</u>. Consult legal counsel if verbal violence falls under the category of violating a protected human right in the workplace.

3. Find out if there is a policy at your medical institution on violence in the workplace. Champion improvements to the policy or help create one if there is no official document so that your institution is a safe space for healing and teaching.

4. Learn nonviolent communication through online resources to restore your empathy and improve your leadership skills. Bring nonviolent communication for medical professionals to your hospital or medical school.

5. Document all verbal violence. Audio or video footage is preferable to a written personal memo. Reference <u>Human Rights Violations Documentation Guidelines</u>.

Document Yelling

_____

_____

_____

_____

_____

_____

_____

_____

_____

_____

_____

_____

Zombification

*The process of dehumanizing a medical trainee
to produce a compliant robotic doctor.*

Students enter medicine with a dream of helping and healing others. To often they are met with abuse, corruption, and an expectation to be good little worker bees for a system that has neither heart nor soul. Medical trainees are methodically dehumanized and their dreams are shattered—often within the first few months of medical school.

I was so disheartened by the cruelty of my medical education that I signed papers to drop out during my first year. Since I had no money to leave (and my tuition and apartment were paid for), my anatomy partner advised, "Just keep taking tests and see what happens." I graduated. He later died by suicide.

Medicine is an apprenticeship profession. We learn to be doctors by studying doctors. We adopt their behaviors and actions as the norm.

Medical education is a grooming process—an indoctrination into a culture that rarely honors or respects the hearts, souls, or dreams of our future physicians. Instead, trainees are subjected to abuse and coerced into being compliant factory workers in what I call assembly-line medicine.

I receive so many emails from disheartened trainees struggling with the inhumanity of their medical education. Here are a few examples:

"So I just walked out of clinic today and I have to tell you I feel awful. Just awful. I was so excited to work at this particular clinic and now having seen how we went through patients like they were scraps to be tossed out, it is so disheartening. The doc I was working with was lovely. She was very nice. But she kept telling me that I was making the 'classic mistake' of trying to ask patients about their problems. Apparently we don't have time for that."

Another doctor shares, "My mentors are kind, but they're also so disconnected. They were clicking through visit logs to point out the 'slacker' docs with 25 patients in an afternoon because we saw 30."

A new trainee in his clinical rotation was told, "You only get sued if you are an asshole, so always pretend to be interested."

Physicians are now being instructed not to ask patients, "How are you?" because open-ended questions waste time during a seven-minute office visit. "We are now to be double-booked [two patients per appointment slot] to make our production quotas," explains one distraught doctor. "Our regional director (not a doctor) reinforced the decision by our medical director (an MD under the thumb of the regional director) that we are not to ask open-ended questions in our visits but to let the medical assistants who room the patients identify the single issue that they are coming in for and that's it. So we basically need to shut down to whisk them through the door."

An administrator who quit his job shared, "We annihilated the physician-patient relationship for nothing but the sake of revenue. Ruthless commercialization."

Our biggest threat to doctors is the industrialization of medicine leading to mass dehumanization of trainees and the slick third parties swooping in to "save us" from the system dysfunction for the sake of profit.

As a physician employee in a big-box clinic, I was so miserable—even suicidal. Then I did something really crazy—I asked my patients for help. I invited them to design an ideal clinic for us. They shared 100 pages of their most creative ideas. We adopted 90 percent of their feedback and opened our community clinic one month later—the first ideal clinic designed entirely by patients. I am happy, fulfilled, and earning more that I did as a physician employee—and I've never turned any patient away for lack of money since launching our community clinic in 2005.

I'm a womb-to-tomb, till-death-do-us-part physician. My dream of being a small-town family doc doing house calls was way too big for my little cubicle. So I left my cubicle. You can do the same.

TAKE ACTION NOW

1. If your dream is bigger than your cubicle, leave your cubicle. You can practice medicine your way—as an employee, a business owner, or an entrepreneur. Reference free resources on how to launch your ideal clinic at IdealMedicalCare.org.

2. Never let anyone steal your dream. You are paying tuition to receive training to live your dream, not to be a factory worker on an assembly line. Resist.

3. Avoid advice from cynical doctors who have lost their dreams. Wounded from their own training, they are the least resourced to be able to help you live your dreams in medicine.

4. Find a trusted mentor who you respect—a physician practicing medicine joyfully. Ask for guidance. You too can enjoy practicing medicine.

5. Document all efforts on the part of your medical institution to force you to practice medicine unsafely.

Document Zombification & Dehumanization

_____

_____

_____

_____

_____

_____

_____

_____

_____

_____

Conclusion

When I finished writing this action guide, I felt relief, then anger.

My singular goal is to end medical student and doctor suicides. I don't want one more mother to endure the loss of her brilliant child. So I wrote this book to offer victims of human rights violations in medicine options (other than suicide) for resolving their pain.

Physicians often tell me, "Keep up the good fight." My suicide work isn't a fight; it's a labor of love. I love honoring my brothers and sisters in medicine who have died by suicide. I am privileged to lead their vigils, memorials, even retreats for grieving families. I am dedicated to helping suicidal doctors and medical students. *But wouldn't it be great if nobody needed my help?* Imagine, no more suffering. No more suicides.

But what if I publish this book and nobody does anything?

A cycle of abuse is maintained by a victim, perpetrator, and rescuer. I've been all three. Like most physicians, I entered medical school with a dream to heal the wounded. Then, I was wounded by my medical training. I adapted by depriving myself of food, water, and sleep. I worked multi-day shifts even when sick and, like most doctors, I wore my self-abuse as a badge of honor. I became my own perpetrator.

I distrusted doctors. I adopted the language of my oppressors. I used gaslighting words that blamed doctors. My distrust of doctors led predictably to very few physician friends. After training, I felt trapped in assembly-line clinics with other miserable doctors. We bonded over our shared suffering and disempowerment. We complained about our noncompliant patients who lacked motivation for behavior change. We bitched when patients went doctor shopping from doctor to doctor while we went job hopping from job to job.

One day I realized nobody was coming to save me.

I had to save myself. And I did. In 2004, I quit my employed job and launched my own ideal clinic. I became rescuer. Since then, I've been rescuing medical students and doctors.

Now I'm asking for help.

I'm no longer interested in playing victim, perpetrator, or rescuer. The cycle of abuse in medicine is so entrenched it's accepted as normal. Persecutors attack victims. Victims search for rescuers. I've served as physician rescuer for 15 years. Now this action guide provides victims with the skills to persecute their own persecutors who will then become victims—and the cycle continues. Thus my anger and frustration. To break our cycle of abuse we must step out of the roles of victim, persecutor, and rescuer—together. We all have the power to save ourselves.

Blaming persecutors is easy and short-sighted. Yet persecutors would not exist without victims, and victims can't exist without persecutors. In medicine, our persecutors were once victims of the same human rights violations we pass down to each new generation of physicians. As doctors we are natural rescuers. Thus, all of us have the potential to be victim, perpetrator, and rescuer—at the same time—and this is what keeps us all stuck.

To overcome our cycle of abuse as physicians we must understand the truth about ourselves—how we may have participated in the abuse. Now is not the time to complain about injustice to those who are powerless to help us. Nobody is coming to save us—except us.

You Will Likely Have One of Four Reactions to this Book

1. **FIGHT**. You will disagree with this book. You will dislike my premise and discredit me among physicians. You will perpetuate human rights violations by fueling the current abuse cycle.

2. **FLIGHT**. You will agree with this book. You have witnessed human rights violations in medicine. You have seen others injured by abuse and you decided to do nothing. You will decide to do nothing now and remain complicit in the abuse cycle.

3. **FREEZE**. You will agree with this book. You have witnessed human rights violations in medicine. You have seen others injured by abuse and you decided to do something as a rescuer such as becoming a "burnout" coach, yet your actions may have kept victims and persecutors stuck in the abuse cycle. Reference <u>Gaslighting</u>.

4. **FREE YOURSELF**. You will agree with this book. You have witnessed human rights violations in medicine. You have seen others injured by abuse and you decided to do nothing. Now you choose to take action to liberate yourself and others from the abuse cycle.

Writing *Human Rights Violations in Medicine* has been an act of love. I encourage you to join me in self love by taking action now. By breaking free from the cycle of abuse, you are loving yourself, your patients, and our profession—and you will find your way back to loving your life as a doctor as I have.

Meditation gardens, yoga, and deep breathing are not treatments for human rights violations. Legal force and financial penalties will work wonders, as will removing persecutors from power, victims from powerlessness—and restoring our ability as individual doctors to save ourselves.

I wanted to end the book with "get off your ass and do something," but I don't want to victimize you all so I will stop here.

Exercises

The following exercises are designed to help you eradicate the cycle of abuse in medicine.

Thank you for helping heal our beloved profession.

Uncomfortable Situations

STEP 1: Identify the uncomfortable feelings you are experiencing.

Abused	Distraught	Neglected
Afraid	Distrust	Nervous
Alienated	Dread	Numb
Ambivalent	Empty	Overwhelmed
Angry	Enraged	Panicked
Anxious	Envious	Powerless
Apathetic	Exasperated	Regretful
Ashamed	Exhausted	Rejected
Awkward	Frazzled	Resentful
Belittled	Fearful	Sad
Betrayed	Frustrated	Scared
Bitter	Grief	Shocked
Bored	Guilt	Suspicious
Challenged	Helpless	Tense
Confused	Hopeless	Terrified
Defeated	Humiliated	Trapped
Deprived	Hurt	Unappreciated
Detached	Inadequate	Uncertain
Devastated	Incompetent	Undermined
Disappointed	Indifferent	Undervalued
Disconnected	Insecure	Unsure
Discouraged	Insignificant	Uptight
Disgusted	Isolated	Weak
Disillusioned	Lonely	Withdrawn
Disrespected	Miserable	Worried

STEP 2: Write about situations that evoke your uncomfortable feelings and identify any corresponding human rights violations.

_____

_____

_____

_____

_____

_____

_____

_____

_____

_____

_____

_____

_____

_____

_____

_____

_____

_____

_____

_____

_____

_____

_____

_____

_____

_____

_____

Exercises: Uncomfortable Situations

Victim

STEP 1: Identify uncomfortable situations when you have been in the role of the victim.

_____

_____

_____

_____

_____

_____

_____

_____

_____

_____

_____

_____

_____

_____

_____

_____

_____

_____

_____

_____

STEP 2: Match with corresponding human rights violations and claim how you will take action to disengage from the victim role.

_____

_____

_____

_____

_____

_____

_____

_____

_____

_____

_____

_____

_____

_____

_____

_____

_____

_____

_____

_____

_____

_____

_____

_____

Exercises: Victim

Persecutor

STEP 1: Identify uncomfortable situations
when you have been in the role of the persecutor.

_____

_____

_____

_____

_____

_____

_____

_____

_____

_____

_____

_____

_____

_____

_____

_____

_____

_____

_____

_____

_____

_____

STEP 2: Match with corresponding human rights violations and claim how you will take action to disengage from the persecutor role.

_____

_____

_____

_____

_____

_____

_____

_____

_____

_____

_____

_____

_____

_____

_____

_____

_____

_____

_____

_____

_____

_____

_____

_____

_____

_____

_____

Rescuer

STEP 1: Identify uncomfortable situations when you have been in the role of the rescuer.

_____

_____

_____

_____

_____

_____

_____

_____

_____

_____

_____

_____

_____

_____

_____

_____

_____

_____

_____

_____

_____

_____

STEP 2: Match with corresponding human rights violations and claim how you will take action to disengage from the rescuer role.

_____

_____

_____

_____

_____

_____

_____

_____

_____

_____

_____

_____

_____

_____

_____

_____

_____

_____

_____

_____

_____

_____

_____

_____

_____

_____

_____

Letters

STEP 1: Identify and name the other people involved while you have been playing the roles of victim, persecutor, and rescuer.

Victim	Persecutor	Rescuer

STEP 2: Write a letter to each person you believe has harmed you or that you may have harmed. (Choose to send it to them or not.)

Dear _____,

_____

_____

_____

_____

_____

_____

_____

_____

_____

_____

_____

_____

_____

_____

_____

_____

_____

_____

_____

_____

_____

_____

Sincerely,

_____

Dear _____,

_____

_____

_____

_____

_____

_____

_____

_____

_____

_____

_____

_____

_____

_____

_____

_____

_____

_____

_____

_____

Sincerely,

_____

Dear _____,

_____

_____

_____

_____

_____

_____

_____

_____

_____

_____

_____

_____

_____

_____

_____

_____

_____

_____

_____

_____

_____

Sincerely,

_____

Dear _____,

_____

_____

_____

_____

_____

_____

_____

_____

_____

_____

_____

_____

_____

_____

_____

_____

_____

_____

_____

_____

Sincerely,

_____

Dear _____,

_____

_____

_____

_____

_____

_____

_____

_____

_____

_____

_____

_____

_____

_____

_____

_____

_____

_____

_____

_____

Sincerely,

_____

Addendum to My Hippocratic Oath

STEP 1: Check the experiences you have endured and claim your ***Wible Human Rights Violations Inventory Number (WHR-VIN).***

____ Anti-Assembly

____ Bullying

____ Censorship

____ Confidentiality Breach

____ Corruption

____ Discrimination, Mental Health Disability

____ Discrimination, Physical Disability

____ Discrimination, Racial

____ Discrimination, Sexual

____ Exploitation

____ Food Deprivation

____ Forced Drugging

____ Gaslighting

____ Harassment, Disability

____ Harassment, Racial

____ Harassment, Sexual

____ Hazing

____ Illegal Activity

____ Intimidation

____ J-1 Visa Abuse

____ Joking

____ Karōshi & Karojishi

____ Lying

____ Maternal Deprivation

____ No Mental Health Care

____ Overwork

____ Pimping

____ Punishment when Sick

____ Question Quashing

____ Retaliation

____ Sleep Deprivation

____ Suicide (Attempt or Ideation)

____ Termination, Wrongful

____ Threat

____ Unethical Activity

____ Violence

____ Water Deprivation

____ Xenophobia

____ Yelling

____ Zombification

____ ***TOTAL WHR-VIN***

STEP 2: Complete your Addendum to your Hippocratic Oath.

My Name is: _____

During my medical training and career I have experienced ___ human rights violations. I am now ready to heal. Here are the action steps I will take now:

_____

_____

_____

_____

_____

_____

_____

_____

_____

_____

_____

_____

_____

_____

_____

_____

_____

_____

_____

_____

Signature: _____ Date: _____

Notes

Notes

Notes

Notes

Pamela Wible, M.D., practices family medicine in an ideal clinic designed entirely by her patients in Oregon where she still does housecalls. In between caring for patients, Dr. Wible helps physicians launch independent clinics nationwide. She operates a free suicide hotline and has helped countless medical students and physicians heal from anxiety, depression, PTSD, and suicidal thoughts so they can enjoy practicing medicine again. She has investigated nearly 1,300 doctor suicides and her extensive database and suicide registry reveals highest-risk specialties—and solutions. Dr. Wible speaks widely on innovative practice models and physician suicide prevention. She is author of *Pet Goats & Pap Smears: 101 Medical Adventures to Open Your Heart & Mind, Physician Suicide Letters—Answered,* and *Human Rights Violations in Medicine: A-to-Z Action Guide.* Contact her at IdealMedicalCare.org.

Made in the USA
Columbia, SC
21 June 2019